'Never has there been such a woman!'

'Look, you brought me here. I didn't ask to come.' Beth glared at Jay angrily. 'I would have been quite content to go back in the helicopter and——'

'But I—I would not be content with that.' Jay leant forward suddenly and took one of her hands, turning it over in the palm of his while his other hand stroked the base of her wrist softly. 'I want more, much more.'

Dear Reader

As spring moves into summer, you can't help but think about summer holidays, and to put you in the right frame of mind this month's selection is jam-packed with exotic holiday destinations. As a tempter, why not try Patricia Wilson's new Euromance, DARK SUNLIGHT, set in sultry Spain? *And*, who knows, you may well find yourself one day visiting the very places mentioned in the novel! One thing's for sure, you're bound to have lots of fun on the way...

The Editor

Helen Brooks lives in Northamptonshire and is married with three children. As a committed Christian, busy housewife and mother, spare time is at a premium, but her hobbies include reading, swimming and walking her comical and very lovable old dog. Her long-cherished aspiration to write became a reality when she put pen to paper on reaching the age of forty, and sent the result off to Mills & Boon.

Recent titles by the same author:

STONE ANGEL
CRUEL CONSPIRACY
GENTLE SAVAGE

COLD
FIRE

BY

HELEN BROOKS

MILLS & BOON LIMITED
ETON HOUSE   18-24 PARADISE ROAD
RICHMOND   SURREY   TW9 1SR

First published in Great Britain 1993
by Mills & Boon Limited

© Helen Brooks 1993

Australian copyright 1993
Philippine copyright 1993
This edition 1993

ISBN 0 263 78034 1

Set in Times Roman 10 on 11½ pt.
01-9306-58080 C

Made and printed in Great Britain

CHAPTER ONE

'GOOD afternoon, Miss Kerri. I will begin this interview with the same question I have put to the other six applicants before you. What makes you think you are special enough to warrant being employed in my service?'

As Beth faltered nervously to a surprised halt in the middle of the huge hotel room she stared dumbly at the jet-black head of the man seated in the large swivel chair with his back towards her.

'Well?' The heavily accented voice was arrogantly patient but her finely tuned ears picked up the thread of irritation in the deep, rich tones, and burning hot colour stained her pale cheeks a vivid shade of pink.

What a truly ignorant pig! He couldn't even be bothered to turn and look at her as he spoke. Her senses took note of the expensively furnished room and luxurious surroundings at the same time as her mind searched for an adequately scathing reply. She did need this job badly, but not that badly!

'I wouldn't presume to try and influence your judgement, Señor de Rojas, with the trivia of mere words.' Her voice was icy and very controlled. 'You have my credentials in the folder in front of you, I believe. I suggest you examine them. I am quite content to let my qualifications speak for me.' There was total heavy silence for a long moment and then the big dark figure turned slightly in the chair so that he was half facing her in profile.

'And if I am not content?'

She shrugged gracefully with a small tilt to her blonde head. 'If there are any points on which you are not clear I would be happy to try and answer your queries . . .' The wide shoulders stiffened at her overt refusal to be intimidated and she sighed mentally. That was it, then; she had blown it now for sure. Well, she only had herself to blame. The agency had warned her he was a difficult client, having already interviewed most of their staff with a terseness that apparently bordered on interrogation. The Swifte agency had the well-earned reputation of supplying people of only the very highest calibre in their limited field of tutors and companions; it was unheard of for any of their personnel to be rejected. This man had refused six of them.

'I see.' The dark liquid voice gave nothing away, and still he didn't look directly at her. 'It would appear the—how do you say?—the ball is back in my court?'

She bit hard on her lower lip. His remark, said with such cool blandness, had taken her by surprise, and she didn't know how to reply. It didn't help matters either that he was in deep shadow behind the large walnut desk, owing to carefully positioned lighting, whereas she was in the full glare of the chandelier directly overhead. She should have continued to the desk when she first came into the room; at least she would have been able to see to whom she was talking then. As it was, she was at a distinct disadvantage of her own making.

'Would you care to be seated?' It was as though he had read her mind. She nodded with a deference she was far from feeling and moved quickly to the seat opposite him, becoming aware as she did so that the profile revealed to her was quite stunningly attractive, the tanned brown skin and jet-black hair perfectly complemented by the fine aquiline nose and hard, almost cruel mouth.

'Now, then.' He turned, slowly and deliberately, as he spoke to face her fully, and she was shocked to see that the left side of his face was marred by a long white scar that stretched down from just under his eye to below the square jaw. The effect should have been disfiguring, but on the dark, handsome face it added an air of harsh piracy that was undeniably sensual. She felt her stomach muscles contract and her charcoal-grey eyes widened and flickered.

'It bothers you, Miss Kerri?' He touched his face briefly, his eyes tight on hers. She realised now that all his previous actions had been leading up to this moment, the movement premeditated rather than instinctive. He had clearly been in some sort of horrific accident and for reasons known only to himself wanted her reaction to his injury.

She took a deep breath and forced her eyes to remain on his as she answered slowly and honestly, 'No, Señor de Rojas, it doesn't bother me. I happen to feel that it's usually the scars that are not visible that cause the most distress. Physical injury could happen to any of us; unfortunately it's part of life and must be dealt with as such.'

Her face was clear and open as his slanted green gaze raked the pure features in long, considering perusal. She hoped she hadn't sounded uncaring. She hadn't meant to, but somehow the natural reaction of pity was quite absent from her mind. This man didn't inspire such an emotion, rather——

The deep modulated voice interrupted her thoughts. 'How much do you know about the position for which you are applying?' The English was very correct and formal, almost stilted, but she sensed she had passed the first test.

She gathered her errant thoughts and tried to concentrate whole-heartedly on the task in hand. If she wanted this job, and suddenly she wasn't at all sure that she did, she had to appear in full control of herself and articulate and direct. She knew instinctively that he was a man who suffered fools badly.

'Very little.' She cleared her throat slightly. 'I have been ... on holiday, and only got back to London yesterday. The agency rang at ten o'clock this morning with the barest of details and here I am.' If he noticed the hesitation he didn't comment on it. 'They informed me merely that a Señor de Rojas required an English companion-tutor to his nephew for the next twelve months until the boy is ready to come to a private school here. I understand I will be required to live in Mexico, but that if the circumstances warranted it I would be free at any time to return to England.' She glanced at his silent, closed face. He had moved slightly again so that the scar was not so visible but she sensed there was no false vanity involved, more a wish to put her at ease.

'*Sí.*' He thought for a moment, obviously considering his next words. 'As with any post, there is more to it than that. Do you wish the interview to continue?' The question brought a start of surprise she was unable to conceal and a glimmer of a smile twisted the firm lips for a fleeting moment.

'Of course.' Her voice was quiet.

'I had the impression you were ... apprehensive, Miss Kerri?' The dark gaze dared her to disagree.

'It would be unwise of me to dash headlong into a situation,' she replied stiffly. 'I always like to ascertain exactly what will be required of me.'

'Good.' They were both aware she had skirted his oblique question. 'I dislike impetuosity, but it is a trait I have found rarely to excess in the English.'

As the green eyes swept over her silver-blonde hair and pale skin she felt there was something in their depths that was disconcerting, almost sinister, but the thought was gone in an instant as he settled back in his chair and began to speak. 'My nephew is nine years old, Miss Kerri, and is suffering from a certain degree of... agitation. His parents were killed in a car accident almost two years ago and he was with them at the time. It was most distressing.' The cold voice was quite expressionless as though he were commenting on the cricket score. 'We thought he would settle eventually, but that does not seem to be the case, and as he is due to start school in England in barely twelve months I feel an English tutor is necessary. He was in hospital for some time after the accident and found it difficult to adjust on his return home to a changed household. His behaviour is, at times, most unsatisfactory.'

Beth felt a swift rush of anger at this man's heartlessness. He was talking about his nephew as though he were a piece of furniture for which he had paid an inordinate amount of money only to find it damaged on delivery. 'That's regrettable.' The trace of sarcasm in her soft voice brought his eyes snapping up to meet her innocent stare, and after a long, searching glance he lowered his eyes to the papers on his desk, obviously unsure as to whether there was any intended criticism in her remark or not.

'Quite.' He picked up a neatly typewritten piece of paper which she recognised as her agency particulars. 'I see that the last child you taught for any length of time was disabled.'

'Yes.' Beth tried to speak quietly and rationally although her heart leapt into her mouth. She wasn't ready to face any probing questions about Samantha yet; the wound was still too raw.

'You left there because...?' He paused to let her answer and she licked dry lips quickly, noticing that the small, nervous gesture was not lost on those piercing eyes watching her every move.

'The little girl died.' She was relieved to find that her voice was not reflecting the trembling in the pit of her stomach.

'This should have been noted——' He caught himself with a little shake of his head. 'I am very sorry, Miss Kerri, I had not been informed. I have no wish to ask questions that are painful, but...?'

'That's all right.' She lowered her head and noticed her hands were bunched into tight fists on her lap. Relax, relax. She forced her clenched fingers to unwind and took a deep breath as she raised her head again, her sleek blonde hair swinging in its smooth bob as she did so. 'It was inevitable.'

'That is of no help when the worst actually happens.' He swung round in his chair with his back towards her as he spoke and for a few tense moments silence reigned. The room was warm with the effects of hothouse central heating and Beth found that she was beginning to feel quite faint. She should have eaten lunch, should have forced something past the lump in her throat that seemed to have been there forever but in reality had appeared that devastating night nine weeks ago when Samantha died.

'You have had experience with difficult children?'

'I'm sorry?' She looked up dazedly, realising he was facing her again and speaking. She hadn't heard a word.

'Your last position, it would not have been easy. The child would have been difficult at times?' His voice was cold.

'Samantha was wonderful.' She was looking at him now from a great distance; his dark face seemed to sway slightly as she tried to keep her eyes on his. 'But there was a little boy before her with learning problems; he could be quite a handful.'

'Miss Kerri, are you feeling quite well?' She vaguely heard the deep, low voice through the buzzing in her ears but as she made to reply her brain would not form the words coherently. As the floor rushed up to meet her in a big black wave part of her mind was aware of sudden movement behind the desk and then the darkness took over, and she felt herself carried inwards in a rushing tide of confused noise and clamour as her overloaded senses took refuge in the only way they knew how.

She came round to find herself lying on an upholstered chaise-longue with the most disgusting smell being wafted under her nostrils. She turned her head violently as she put up a hand in murmuring protest, and immediately the smell was gone as the room geared into focus. Señor de Rojas was kneeling by her side, his arm supporting her head, and someone—a maid by the uniform—was bending over her with a small vial in her hand. 'It's only smelling salts, miss,' the young girl said cheerfully. 'Señor de Rojas rang to say you had fainted.'

'I'm so sorry.' As a flood of burning humiliation swept fierce colour into chalk-white cheeks Beth struggled to sit up, her head swimming and her legs curiously weak. 'I've never done this before in my life. I don't know what to say...'

Señor de Rojas stood up slowly, his cold face imperturbable, and she waited miserably for the polite rejection that was to follow. 'Have you eaten today?'

'I'm sorry?' Beth looked up at him in bewilderment.

'You are as thin as a reed. It was like carrying a small child in my arms.' As the full import of the quiet words hit home, the colour that had just began to subside returned again with renewed vigour. He had held her, carried her, while she had been unconscious. There was something almost indecent in the thought, although she couldn't have explained why. 'Have you had a meal today?' He was persistent and she forced herself to shake her head slowly.

'I didn't want anything; there wasn't time...'

'Rubbish!' The heavy accent took away the sting from the word. 'Geraldine, you will bring the tea trolley a little early today. Two cups, please. *Gracias*.'

As the small maid hurried away Beth gathered her wits sufficiently to smooth her hair and adjust her dishevelled clothing, making a stumbling protest as she did so. 'I really can't impose on you any further, Señor de Rojas; there is no need... You've been very kind...'

'You are here for an interview, are you not?' The handsome, branded face was in the light and very close now, and Beth caught her breath again as she looked up into the bright, glittering gaze. In spite of the scar he really was the most magnificent man she had ever seen. The brownness of his skin intensified the clear flecked green of his eyes, and the straight black hair was longer than most men wore it, flicking into the bottom of his neck and stopping just short of his shoulders. He was very lean, but the big shoulders spoke of considerable strength and he was tall, very tall. At a guess, six feet four, Beth mused consideringly. The amusement in the green gaze suddenly informed her that she was staring and she lowered her eyes quickly, her face crimson with embarrassment.

'I'm sorry.'

'I have noticed it is a failing with you English, the need to apologise when it is not necessary.'

'Look, Señor de Rojas, I really don't think——'

'Jay.'

'I'm sorry?' She had said the words before she'd thought, and she noticed the mocking quirk to the hard mouth with a little dart of resentment.

'My name is Jay,' he said slowly. 'I really think if we are going to share tea together it would be more comfortable if we were a little less formal.' His voice was cool and even as though he were issuing an order that he expected to be obeyed without question. 'Your name is Beth?' His accent made the name she had always disliked for its plainness infinitely attractive.

'Yes, but——'

A light knock at the door announced the arrival of the tea trolley, and the same little maid entered, her face all smiles. 'Here you are, sir.' She wheeled the trolley across to the large coffee-table and proceeded to place the contents on its glass surface. 'Would you like me to pour——?'

'Thank you but no, Geraldine.' He dismissed the girl with a warm smile that brought a slight flush to the round cheeks as she scurried from the room. The table was positively groaning with the array of wafer-thin sandwiches and fresh cream cakes it was holding, besides delicious-looking scones, several varieties of jam and two types of fruit cake. There was a pot of steaming coffee and a smaller squat one which she presumed held tea.

'Coffee or tea?' He knelt down by the low table as he spoke and Beth was suddenly acutely aware of stretched material pulled tight over muscled, hard thighs.

'Oh, let me; I should——'

He cut off her embarrassment with a cool order. 'Sit still, please, Beth. I would prefer that you try and relax. Now, tea or coffee? And you will tell me what you like to eat.'

She looked at him helplessly and then answered him in subdued tones. She had never liked masterful men;

she had found in the past that that particular attribute was usually an indication of insensitivity and bullishness, although she was honest enough to admit to herself that her father had probably coloured her view of the male sex in that area. He had been a brute of a man and when he had died her main feeling had been one of extreme relief. She had always been amazed that her mother had stayed with him until the bitter end.

As she struggled slowly through the heaped plate of food she could feel his eagle eyes sweeping over her once or twice, although he mainly kept his gaze to the wad of papers on his lap, making swift, short notes in the margins as he read. She noticed he had had a cup of coffee, black and hot, but nothing to eat. He had clearly ordered the food just for her. The thought caused her to squirm with embarrassment yet again; he must think she was a complete fool.

'Now, Beth.' He looked up as she finished the last mouthful of food and she had to admit she felt immeasurably better. 'I have no wish to pry into your private affairs, but in view of the fact that you are here seeking employment within my household I think you would agree I must ask you why you appear to be in some...distress. My nephew has his own problems, you understand, *sí*?'

'Of course, Señor de Rojas.' She just couldn't bring herself to use his Christian name. 'Would you prefer me to leave?'

'I would prefer that you confide in me. I can assure you that your disclosure will not go beyond this room. However, if you feel unable...' He waved his hand lazily towards the door. 'My first concern must be for Mateo, you understand.' The handsome face was cold and expressionless, which somehow made it easier. She took a deep breath and started talking.

'I apologise for my behaviour, Señor de Rojas, and I can assure you that if you found me suitable it would not happen again.' Fat chance he would offer her the job now, she thought miserably, but she felt she owed him some sort of an explanation for the travesty of an interview. 'As you guessed, I had not eaten today, which was stupid of me, but I have suffered two bereavements in a short space of time and I'm afraid I've been thrown off course for a while.'

He raised dark, severe eyebrows and waited for her to continue. 'My mother died three months ago after a short illness and within four weeks my small charge, Samantha, also passed away. I took an extended break to try and regain my equilibrium although with hindsight I realise now it was the worst thing I could have done. I should have got back into the stream of life at once.'

He nodded slowly. 'I see.'

'I feel I am ready to work again, more than ready, and could give your nephew the best I have to offer. My qualifications——'

'*Sí, sí.*' He waved his hand to stop her. 'Your suitability on that score is without question or you would not be here now.' He paused, his heavily lashed eyes tight on her pale face. 'The rest of your family? How do they feel about the possibility of you leaving the country after such traumatic circumstances?'

'I have no other family, *señor.*' She didn't know where the strength was coming from to speak so calmly and coolly but she was immensely grateful for it. 'I was an only child and my father died two years ago.'

'You have obviously encountered great sorrow in your short life.' The green eyes stroked her face consideringly. 'You are only twenty-five now?'

'Yes.' She looked him full in the face as she spoke.

'I am a great believer in the old adage that one must sample the pot to give an opinion of the contents. You understand me?'

'I think so,' she said doubtfully and he smiled suddenly, causing her breath to catch in a tight knot in her throat. It transformed the cold, shadowed face like the sun on a winter's afternoon.

'The other applicants I have seen were most suitable,' his voice was dry, 'but without the understanding I feel Mateo is in need of at the moment. He needs a sympathetic companion but, more than that, someone who understands, really understands, what he is going through. He is a very sensitive child and that cannot be allowed to develop into flawed weakness through misguided handling, or smothered by brutality. He needs both compassion and discipline, tenderness and, when necessary, extreme firmness. Your job will be difficult and time-consuming and at times quite heartbreaking. Do you think you are up to it?'

'I am sure I am.' This time there was no uncertainty in her voice and he smiled slowly again.

'He needs a woman's touch, you understand, but no moddle-coddling.' His variation of the last word would have made her laugh in other circumstances. 'Mateo will inherit his father's ranch and the adjoining land when he is grown and it will take a hard and intelligent man to run successfully such a concern. His mother——' now his eyes turned into chips of cold emerald '—spoilt him unmercifully. I will have none of that.'

'Yes, I understand, Señor de Rojas.'

'Jay, *por favor*.' It was not a request.

'I need to know——' She stopped abruptly, fearing he would think she was being unduly nosy, considering she had not been offered the post.

'*Sí?*' The dark face was enquiring.

'The accident. How much did Mateo see? Was he aware——?'

'It was as bad as it could be.' He turned from her so that the marred side of his face was hidden and a small taut muscle clenched in his square jaw. 'Karen, his mother, she was driving and——'

'Karen?' She interrupted him with a surprised frown, expecting a more Spanish-sounding name.

'She was English.' There was no expression in the cool voice but somehow she knew immediately that there had been no love lost between Mateo's mother and her brother-in-law. 'Alfredo, my brother, was sitting beside his wife in the front seat and Mateo was strapped in the back. They had only gone a mile or so from their home when the vehicle overturned. Karen was... upset at the time and misjudged a curve in the road. I was following on behind——' Beth sensed there was more, much more that he wasn't telling her '—and by the time I reached them the engine was on fire.'

He paused for a moment but the deep voice was quite calm when he continued. 'Karen was clearly dead, Alfredo's legs were trapped and he was screaming at me to get Mateo out. The doors were locked, the windscreen smashed, and I wasn't too careful in the circumstances. Hence——' He touched his face briefly. 'A piece of jagged metal I didn't notice. I got the boy out and went back for my brother. I was a few yards away when the car exploded. Mateo saw it all.'

'Oh, no.' Her voice was a horrified murmur. 'How awful.'

'Nevertheless, Miss Kerri, it is in the past.' He looked at her tightly, fixing her with his piercing eyes. 'My nephew must learn to rise above his natural emotions. It is imperative he learns to fly, like a bird, above that which would destroy him. I cannot always take care of his business interests as well as my own. He has to learn to stand on his own two feet.'

'He's a little boy!' The protest was involuntary.

'He will grow into a man.' The green gaze was unrelenting. 'There is no room for weakness in the world which he inhabits.'

'Do you live on the ranch?' she asked warily. She was beginning to feel that they were from different planets.

'I have my own ranch which adjoins Mateo's property. For the moment Mateo is living with me and will continue to do so until he leaves for the boarding-school in England his mother organised.'

'I see.' She was finding she didn't like this Señor de Rojas at all.

'Another cup of tea?'

She stared at him in amazement. Here they were talking about life and death in the most tragic circumstances, and he could switch to asking her if she required more tea in the same breath. He was the coldest, hardest man she had ever met and suddenly she felt desperately sorry for the little Mateo, all alone under this man's care. He probably made his nephew's life a misery.

She shook her head in answer to his question, veiling her eyes against the cruel face, but his next words showed her that she hadn't been quick enough in concealing her thoughts from the razor-sharp gaze.

'You think I am hard?' he asked grimly. 'Well, you are absolutely right and I intend that Mateo should be the same. He has inherited a small part of a beautiful country that will eat him alive if he does not master it.'

She looked at him without replying. He was everything she disliked and despised in a man: arrogant, overbearing, cruel and unfeeling. Just like her father, in fact.

'You think I exaggerate? No matter.' He showed his strong white teeth in a mocking smile. 'Your opinion is of no importance. I rule my household, and that of my nephew's, how I see fit. I do not countenance any interference and I will not tolerate defiance.' He glanced at her as she sat, fair-haired and pale, her grey eyes huge in a white face, and she could almost read his thoughts. He thought she was fragile and malleable, that she would give him no trouble and be a gentle, understanding mother-figure to the troubled little boy who was his nephew. Well, the last part was true enough. She raised her chin unconsciously as she followed her thoughts. But if he offered her this job, and she doubted that very much, she would accept it, grasp it with both hands.

Her main reason for applying for this post had been to escape a country that for the moment held too many painful memories that were always on the surface of her mind. But now that seemed almost unimportant compared to the tragedy that was little Mateo. But his uncle would find that she was not some sort of hired servant to do his bidding mindlessly like a medieval peasant. She would deal with Mateo as she saw fit and she sensed, instinctively, that that would bring her into direct conflict with this dangerous, autocratic individual who played with other people's lives as though they were pieces on a giant chessboard.

'You feel you could cope with Mateo?' the cold voice asked.

She looked calmly enough into the glittering, unreadable eyes and nodded slowly. 'Yes, I do, *señor*. As I said when we first met, the scars that are unseen, in the mind, are the worst to deal with, but dealt with they must be.'

He moved his head sharply. 'Exactly. I liked that phraseology. You are the first person I have been inclined to trust my nephew to. He does not need empty platitudes and emotional fussing.'

She veiled her eyes again and looked hastily at her hands. 'Is there anything else you would like to know, Señor de Rojas?'

'Just one thing.' She glanced up and met a mocking twist to the firm lips. 'If I offer you the post, and you accept, do I continue to be Señor de Rojas indefinitely?'

'No, of course not.' She blushed furiously. 'It's just that I'm not used to informality at this stage of an interview. I think——'

'Would you like the job, Miss Kerri?' Her name was said teasingly but not unkindly.

She looked at him for a stunned second. Now the moment was here she knew she did want it, badly, but she had never thought he would offer it to her.

'Yes, please.'

A flash of some emotion that she couldn't name showed fleetingly in the dark face and then he smiled, charmingly, but the smile didn't quite reach those flecked catlike eyes. 'Then it is yours.' He turned away with a deprecating grimace. 'I have never yet offered anyone employment with a view to hearing my name spoken.' She noticed it was his left side of his face that was hidden from her again and sensed, strongly and with total certainty, that it was not because it mattered to him but more to give her time to adjust to his injury.

He was a complex man, but not one whom she would want to even try to understand. He had an aura of almost savage ruthlessness that she found quite repellent, like a vicious black panther that had been let out of its cage to seek prey.

'How soon can you leave England?' She came back to herself with a start and tried to concentrate on the formalities. They spoke for some minutes on the necessary details and then he glanced at the gold watch on his brown wrist, clapping his hand to the side of his face in a gesture of irritation.

'I am sorry.' He inclined his head in apology. 'I am late for an appointment; you will excuse me?'

'Of course.' She rose quickly, more steady now with the plateful of food inside her. That had been kind of him, a little voice said slyly in her head, but she pushed the thought away quickly. It had suited him, that was all.

'If you will phone the hotel tomorrow my secretary will make all the arrangements with you. She only works mornings so please call before lunch.' He clearly wanted her to leave quickly, and she moved swiftly to the door, stopping with a little start as a sharp knock sounded on the outside.

'*Si*?' He opened the door as he spoke, and the tall, slender woman standing in the entrance gave a little cry of pleasure at the sight of him.

'Jay...'

'Felicia, I know I am late; I have been——'

The woman interrupted him with a little giggle as she wound her slim arms round his broad shoulders in a welcome hug, giving a short, sharp bounce to her head that made her long, dark, glossy hair shine like black silk.

'Excuse me.' He turned to Beth with one arm round the woman's tiny waist. 'I would like to introduce you to a dear friend of mine. This is Felicia; Felicia, meet Beth, Mateo's new companion.'

'How—do—you—do?' The woman clearly hadn't Jay's grasp of English and spoke softly and haltingly, looking at Jay under her long lashes beguilingly for approval.

'It's nice to meet you.' Beth smiled as she turned away and walked quickly across the thick wool carpet to the waiting lift. And what sort of good friend are you? she thought irrelevantly as the silent lift sped her downwards. Still, what did it matter? She gave a little shrug of her slim shoulders at her thoughts. He was clearly a man who would be used to female company; some women would find his cool intimidating composure irresistible. But not this one! She was unaware of the bitterness on her face and the way her grey eyes had darkened into blackness.

Aggressive, handsome males were not her style. She had lived too long under her father's tyranny to feel anything but loathing for such men. Her mother had grown old before her time, worn out and broken by her husband's constant womanising and selfish lifestyle, becoming a pathetic little doormat for him to walk over. She could remember various 'good friends' her father had brought home over the years, flaunting his behaviour under his wife's nose. Sometimes the women would be accompanied by their husbands and sometimes not, but she had learnt very early at these gay weekends and intimate dinners to keep quiet and escape to bed as soon as she could.

She gave an imperceptible shake of her head as the lift reached the ground floor. That was in the past now but she had learnt well. She intended to follow her chosen career, see the world and please herself. Her own mistress. She walked out of the large, elegant building without being aware of her surroundings, lost in thought. When she settled down it would be in a small place of her own, with maybe a couple of cats and a dog to keep her company. Her idea of bliss was no commitments and no ties and certainly no overbearing man to tell her black was white and white was black.

She walked on through the crowded London streets full of evening commuters jostling to get home after a hard day's work, unaware of the admiring glances her slim figure and startlingly blonde beauty attracted from more than one pair of predatory male eyes.

No, her thoughts continued, this girl was going to remain her own boss, come hell or high water, and do exactly as she pleased, and if a certain dark green-eyed stranger with his autocratic manner and veiled threats thought he could mould and shape her into being a mere vessel in his exalted employ then he had a severe shock coming! The thought brought a slight smile to her well-shaped lips.

She strode on through the heavy, fume-laden air peculiar to all big cities, aware that she was feeling better than she had done in weeks, but not searching her tender, bruised emotions for a reason why. Probably if she had done so the footsteps might have faltered and the confident tilt to her head dipped, but she didn't. And when later in sleep the image of a fierce, threatening shadow pursued her through the endless corridors of her dreams until she awoke, wet with perspiration and shaking in the chill of the night, still her mind refused to accept the warning her sixth sense was giving her.

She was a successful, independent career girl. She had been in sole charge of her life since escaping from home at the tender age of seventeen; there was no reason to think that this happy state of affairs would change in the foreseeable future, was there? *Was* there?

CHAPTER TWO

'WOULD you care for more coffee?' The polite, disinterested voice of the cool blonde air hostess intruded abruptly into Beth's wandering thoughts as she stared out of the small window in the huge plane.

'No, thank you.' She smiled up at the immaculately groomed girl as she spoke and was rewarded by a formal nod and quick smile.

'We will be landing in just over an hour.' Beth inclined her head in acknowledgement and the girl continued carefully among the first-class seats with her loaded trolley, her practised smile flashing on and off the lovely face like a superior robot.

Señor de Rojas—she still couldn't bring herself to think of him as Jay—had been extremely generous in his dealings with the new English companion to date, she admitted grudgingly, arranging first-class travel in the most luxurious surroundings as though she were a member of his family instead of an employee. She had flown from England to Los Angeles, which had proved exhilarating but exhausting, and then transferred to a smaller plane for the direct flight to Guadalajara in the central highlands of Mexico where she was to be met at the airport by someone called Luis Casteneda. Quite how they would know each other Beth hadn't been informed, and at this moment of time didn't care. She felt lightheaded with a combination of jet-lag and apprehensive excitement, and the thought of a long, warm bath was intensely appealing.

24

'Miss Kerri? I am Luis Casteneda.' Her progress through Customs had been slow and tiring, and now she was barely able to raise a wan smile for the small brown-haired man who was waiting to one side of the air terminal.

'How did you know me?'

The man's soft brown eyes smiled at her as he replied. 'There aren't too many blonde and beautiful English ladies on this flight, *señorita*, and Señor de Rojas gave me a careful description of you.' He took the two heavy cases from her as he spoke. 'Please to follow me.'

The heat outside was not as overpowering as she had expected and Luis caught her look of surprise as she glanced upwards into the clear blue sky. 'You were expecting the fierce sun to bake you without mercy?' She smiled and nodded and he shook his dark head wryly. 'I can see you have a lot to learn about this country, *señorita*. It is big, so big.' He put down her cases and waved his arms in a wide, expansive circle.

'It is a land of Cortés and the Aztecs, of rich silver and copper mines and rolling plains. On the northern plateaux there are the vast cattle ranges and there you have the heat to fry the pure English skin.' His eyes dwelt for a moment on her uncovered arms that looked white in comparison to the brown skins all around her. 'But here—here it is the eternal spring, gentle enough to warm you and tint you a shade of honey that the men will find irresistible.' She flushed scarlet at the look in his eyes and now he laughed out loud, throwing back his head in unaffected amusement. '*Perdóneme, señorita*. I forget the English severity. I meant no offence. I have a daughter your age.'

'That's all right.' She grinned back at him, suddenly warmed by the open friendliness in the sun-lined face. He led the way through a vast car park, his walk lazy and measured to her smaller steps, and then on still further through a maze of buildings on which the sun glimmered and shone with brilliant persistence. In spite of the 'eternal spring' comment she could feel the heat beginning to roast her unclad arms and hastily slipped the light cotton cardigan she had tied casually round her shoulders over their paleness. It must be over eighty degrees, she thought wryly. Obviously the Mexican idea of spring was a world apart from the damp, and often chilly, English version.

'Here we are, *señorita*.' Luis strode over to where a gleaming red and cream helicopter stood baking in the sun, and stowed her cases into its depths.

'What's this?' She stood a few yards away and stared at the small man in amazement.

'Some of the Zoque or Huasteca Indians living in the southern regions would probably refer to it as a big metal bird, *señorita*.' The Mexican's brown eyes were filled with delighted amusement at her surprise. 'Myself, I call it a helicopter.'

'Is it Señor de Rojas's?'

'*Sí, señorita*.' The man was looking at her a little strangely now. 'You are ready?'

'Oh, yes, of course.' She hurried to his side and he helped her up into the hot seat that smelt of burning leather. 'Look, I'm sorry...' She touched Luis's arm hesitantly as he made to start the engine. 'Could I ask you something before we go?'

'*Sí*?'

'Señor de Rojas—he is...very wealthy?' Now she saw that the small man was clearly astounded as he stared at her, his brown eyes stretched wide. 'It's just that there wasn't time to find out much in England. He was called back home unexpectedly the day after he had interviewed me and all the arrangements were made through a hired secretary. She wasn't very forthcoming...' Her voice trailed away at the blank amazement in the Mexican's weathered face. 'I understand the *señor* has a ranch next to that of his nephew's? I suppose they breed cattle or something?'

'Cattle or something?' Luis's face was openly scathing in its contempt. '*Señorita*, the Rojas name is famous throughout the world as the finest stud farm there has ever been or is likely to be.' He was obviously of the opinion that his exalted employer had been grievously insulted by this little slip of an English girl!

'The *señor* can trace his ancestry back to a noble Spanish family with royal connections, and his grandfather and his father before him bred only horses of distinction that were fought for even then. When Señor Jay's father died the estate was divided between his two sons at Señor Jay's request. He is the older brother, you understand, *señorita*?' She looked at him uncomprehendingly. 'Everything was his; he had inherited it all.' The small man's voice was striving for blandness but Beth sensed that he had disapproved of his master's generosity.

'I see.' Her head was beginning to pound, as much with the sudden compilation of data as the stifling heat. 'He must have loved his brother very much to do that.'

'*Sí, señorita.*' Luis's face closed against her and as the rising crescendo of the powerful engine made itself felt she gave up further attempts at conversation. Even through the protective headgear the noise was deafening, muddling her thoughts.

They took off in a wide, graceful curve that left Beth's stomach on the ground, the machine moving swiftly over proud, ornate buildings, tiny flowered courtyards and a busy market that looked gaily foreign. An enormous cathedral dominated the skyline, its magnificent twin bell-towers strange Byzantine creations against the blueness of the Mexican heavens, and as they neared the outskirts of the bustling city she noticed a spectacular ravine, its cavernous depths dizzying. As they flew onwards the lush greenness below amazed her with its fertile, rich beauty; she had expected a dry, arid landscape instead of the small farms and plentiful orchards dotted beneath them.

'Is good, eh?' Luis spoke loudly through his headset and she nodded silently. 'You come at a good time, *señorita*—the rains have just finished.'

As he spoke the small man was dropping the giant machine swiftly downwards, the loss in altitude causing Beth's heart to rise into her mouth. 'The Rojas ranch,' Luis said proudly, inclining his head to the vast green plain stretching below, but Beth could see no sign of life until small dots on the horizon became visible to her searching gaze. As they neared the buildings she saw the hacienda for the first time, a huge, rambling residence with what looked like massive stable blocks about a quarter of a mile behind it.

Everything looked beautifully cared for and immaculately tended, including the large racetrack to one side of the stables. As the helicopter landed on a smooth green lawn in front of the imposing house her stomach lurched nervously. She recognised the tall, dark, commanding figure striding out to meet them.

'*Buenas tardes*, Beth! I trust you had a good journey?' The deep, liquid voice ran over her taut nerves like dark velvet and it took all her will-power to smile as she made a polite conventional reply. In England he had appeared cold, arrogant and proud, and here, in his own domain, he was all that and much more. There was a charisma, a fascination that was openly sensual and magnificently natural and that reached out to her with an allure that shocked her. He was all that she disliked in the male species and yet... She could almost feel the power of his being reaching out to submerge her. This was ridiculous, she chided herself silently as he took her arm in a firm grip and instructed Luis to bring the cases to the house. He was just her employer, for goodness' sake; there was no need to get fanciful even if she was totally exhausted and suffering from a severe case of jet-lag.

Like before, he seemed to read her mind. 'You must be exhausted.' He stood looking down at her, his green eyes unfathomable, but she had stopped to gaze entranced at the house as the full beauty of the hacienda swept over her, and was oblivious to his dark gaze.

The time-worn stonework of the old rambling house was soft and mellow in the afternoon sunlight and liberally covered with a mass of sweet-scented jasmine, purple and red bougainvillaea and dark jade-green ivy, with tubs of flowering shrubs and bright-coloured geraniums adding to the perfumed air. To Beth's tired gaze the low building seemed to stretch forever, a full-length veranda with easy chairs and scattered tables following the roaming shape. Fruit trees of every description surrounded the hacienda; she recognised orange, lemon, apricot and fig but there were others she didn't know, all providing welcome shade and a tantalising fragrance to the rich, soft air.

'It's absolutely lovely. I've never seen such a beautiful place in all my life,' she breathed quietly, and the tall man by her side nodded his black head slowly.

'It is good for Mateo to spend some time here. His own house is a modern structure, not without taste, but still...' The flecked green gaze travelled slowly over the mellow stone as though seeing it for the first time. 'This—this is *la casa*.' The hard mouth moved slightly at her enquiring gaze. 'Home,' he said quietly, and she nodded quickly.

'Can I see Mateo?' she asked eagerly.

'He is spending some time with Felicia's family in Guadalajara and will return tomorrow,' he said absently as he ushered her through the ornate wooden door and into the cool, shaded room beyond. The single-storeyed house was magnificently decorated, the dark, gleaming wood and light, whitewashed walls complemented by superb chandeliers and huge gold-framed pictures, ankle-deep carpeting and discreetly elegant furniture. Beth tried very hard not to gape as Luis placed her two somewhat battered suitcases in the middle of the room they had entered and with a small click of his heels left them.

'I have arranged for a light meal to be served to you in your rooms after you have bathed,' Jay said lazily. 'I would suggest you then sleep for as long as you can. It will take a few days for you to feel fully recovered from the journey, and may I suggest you drink plenty of fluids in the meantime?' She nodded uncertainly, her grey eyes very wide, and he smiled slightly as he picked up the heavy cases as though they contained cotton wool and gestured for her to follow him. 'Juana, my housekeeper, will attend to your needs and inform you of anything you wish to know.'

'Thank you.' Her head was throbbing in earnest now and she followed him through a maze of passageways without really noticing where she was going, stopping as he jerked the brass handle on a door identical to others they had passed and gestured for her to precede him through the open doorway.

The room was simply but expensively furnished in light pastel shades that were restful to the eyes, the gently billowing full-length curtains concealing full-length shuttered doors that led out on to a large paved courtyard green with trees and flowering bushes. 'The *en suite*.'

He opened a door to one side of the wardrobe to reveal a small, gleaming bathroom.

'It's lovely, thank you,' she said weakly as the full realisation of his power and wealth began to make itself felt. He stood looking at her, hard brown hands on jean-clad hips, and she dropped her eyes hastily, terrified that this dark foreigner could read her mind and hating his proud, if natural confidence.

'There is no need to be frightened of me, Beth.' His voice was low and lazy with a richness that sent a shiver shuddering down her spine. She stiffened angrily.

'Frightened?' She raised her head instantly, causing her fair hair to swing in a smooth rush on to scarlet cheeks. 'I'm not frightened of you, Señor de Rojas.' He had touched a nerve she was determined to master.

'No?' His eyes were laughing at her. 'I think maybe I...disturb you, then?'

'Not at all,' she said stoutly, ignoring the quivering in her traitorous limbs as she stared him full in the face.

'*Bueno*. That is good. You will perhaps allow yourself to call me Jay now?' His voice was soft but it was a direct challenge and they both knew it.

'Do your other employees call you by your Christian name?' The narrowed eyes turned into green glass and all amusement left his face as his gaze swept over her, his big body stiffening at her unspoken defiance.

'I thought I had made myself clear in England, Beth.' He moved a step nearer to her as he spoke and she was hotly aware of his great height and the darkness of his tanned skin. 'Here, on the ranch, I rule as I see fit. I am answerable to no one and everyone is answerable to me.' There was a cool arrogance in the calm words that fuelled the small flame of anger ignited by his cold hauteur. 'How I wish you to address me is of concern only to the two of us. Have I made myself clear?'

'Perfectly.' Years of training hid the impotent rage sweeping her body from showing in her flat voice. 'Isn't that a little...dangerous? To be so completely without counsel or advice, I mean?'

He stared silently at her with shuttered eyes until the air grew heavy and her gaze dropped from his in spite of all her efforts to maintain it. 'You are tired, *pequeña*; it has been a long journey.' She was disgusted with herself to find that she was relieved that he had mistaken her outright defiance for exhaustion—that icy green gaze had been unnerving. 'You will now bathe and eat, and then rest.' It wasn't a suggestion and she nodded her agreement with a bent head. 'Juana will be along shortly and Rosa, the maid, will unpack for you.'

'Oh, there's no need for that,' she protested quickly. 'I can see to my things, I'm——'

'*Dios*!' He shook his head as the splinter-sharp gaze raked her smooth face. 'Rosa will see to it!' She realised she had tried his patience to the limit and was wise enough to desist from further resistance as he strode in quick, irritated steps from the room, shutting the door none too gently behind him. What an overbearing, conceited pain of a man!

'Well, that was a brilliant start, Beth, my girl,' she muttered crossly into the empty room as she sank down weakly on to the large, soft bed. 'It might have been better to keep quiet, at least for the first hour.' Tired tears pressed at the back of her eyes as she gazed forlornly round the elegant room. She suddenly felt very small and very alone and started violently as a loud knock sounded outside. 'Come in.'

'I Juana, *señorita. Por favor*?'

'Yes?' When the door still remained closed Beth padded wearily across the room after kicking off her shoes, and as she opened it, it was to see the small, plump housekeeper with her arms full of flowers, struggling to pick up some magazines she had clearly dropped on the floor.

'*Perdóneme, señorita*. The *señor*, he sent these.'

'For me?' Beth knelt down and lifted the pile of glossy magazines and paperbacks off the floor, noticing as she did so that they were all in English, and the flowers in Juana's thick arms were clearly hothouse blooms.

'It to welcome. You understand?' The small woman's little brown face beamed when Beth gave a bemused nod.

'Would you thank Señor de Rojas for me, please?'

'*Sí, sí*. And now you have shower? *Sí*? And I bring you *comida*—the lunch?'

'Thank you.' The hospitality was overwhelming and she could feel the tears back just below the surface of her outwardly calm composure. Jay's gesture had been very thoughtful; he had obviously known she would feel lost and bewildered in a strange country where she knew no one, but she didn't want to think about that right now. The tyrant image was easier to deal with somehow and, besides—her mouth hardened—he would know all the tricks to subdue and dominate a woman. He was just like her father.

She emerged from a long, cool shower in the pretty bathroom feeling relaxed but even more exhausted. She slipped on a light towelling robe before rubbing her thick cap of blonde hair dry; she just couldn't face getting dressed again yet. The catnaps of the last forty-eight hours had caught up with her at last, and every limb ached, the wide, soft bed appearing infinitely inviting.

'The *señor*, he say to eat everything, everything.' Juana bustled into the room after a cursory knock, the small brown-haired girl following her carrying a loaded tray. Beth was relieved to see that the meal was light but tasty—fresh slices of grapefruit, oranges and apricots in natural juice followed by a fluffy omelette and cold meat. Half a bottle of wine was uncorked and ready to pour, and Juana filled the glass to the brim before they left. 'Everything, *señorita*,' she warned as they left, nodding her head like a little brown owl.

Beth could never remember afterwards finishing the meal and getting into bed but she supposed she must have done. Certainly, when she surfaced to childish laughter, a bright morning sun was turning the room into patterned pictures as the long curtains moved gently in the breeze from the open windows, and she realised with a guilty start that she must have been asleep for sixteen hours or more. Whatever would they all think? She struggled to sit up under the scented linen and then sank hastily down again as she did so. The robe had come adrift in the night and she realised she was stark naked under the covers. Supposing someone had come in? But no, they wouldn't, she comforted herself quickly. There would have been no need.

'I want to see her, Gran Jay.' The high, childish voice held a touch of pleading and sounded almost as though someone were in the room with her. She realised it came from the courtyard beyond the open windows. The wooden shutters were still bolted in place from her side of the room, but with the long glass doors open the sound filtered through easily.

'When she wakes up, Mateo. It was a long journey. You must be patient.' The deep voice she recognised. The child's voice spoke again in gabbled Spanish until it was abruptly halted.

'English, Mateo!' Jay's voice had lost the faintly indulgent note it had first held. 'You must learn to think in English or your time there will be miserable.'

'It will be miserable anyway.' The small voice was flat. 'I don't want to leave the ranch, Gran Jay; I don't want to go and——'

'Enough.' It was just one word but she could imagine the look that accompanied it. 'We have had this conversation before. It was your parents' wish that you be educated in England when you are ten. You know this.' Jay's voice was icy and she winced.

She couldn't hear the rest of the conversation as footsteps told her they were leaving, but she had heard enough to cause her heart to sink. If Mateo didn't want to go to England when he was ten and her reason for being here was to get him ready for just that occasion it didn't bode well for their future relationship, and how could his uncle be so cruel and hard with him?

She showered and dressed quickly in a plain white top and light cotton trousers, pausing only to brush her hair into its smooth, shiny bob before she left the room. Once in the passageway she paused uncertainly. The corridor stretched on endlessly either side of her and she didn't have a clue which way to go.

'*Buenos dias, señorita.*' The small maid of the day before came out of a room some way down the passageway with an armful of crumpled linen and made to disappear in the opposite direction.

'Oh, please.' Beth found herself scurrying after the small girl. 'Can you tell me where the *señor* is? Which way do I go?'

'No understand, *señorita*.' The girl clearly didn't speak English and Beth was gazing at her helplessly when that rich velvet voice sounded just behind her.

'The Sleeping Beauty has awakened?'

She spun round so quickly that she almost landed in Jay's arms, and his hands made an involuntary movement towards her before falling easily to his sides again. 'I'm sorry, I've been asleep so long, I didn't realise, and I didn't know which way to go...' She was babbling, she suddenly realised with horror. He would think he had employed a mindless idiot to take care of his nephew. The plain fact was that the sight of him had unnerved her somewhat. Close to, his height seemed formidable and, added to the fresh, lemony fragrance that seemed to come off his skin, and to the fact that he was wearing a shirt that was unbuttoned at the collar revealing several inches of broad, hair-covered chest, the whole effect was one of uncompromising maleness.

'That is perfectly all right, Beth.' His voice was quiet but there was a mocking quirk to the well-shaped mouth as though he knew how he unsettled her. 'I wanted you to sleep. It is important that you meet Mateo for the first time feeling calm and rested.'

Well, the rested part was true, she thought silently, but with that cool, dark face watching her every move the calmness would be purely cosmetic. 'Can I meet him now?'

He gave an imperceptible nod. 'Of course. Would you prefer to eat first? Breakfast has been finished for some time but I understand a tray has been prepared for you and is ready to serve.' He seemed to be obsessed with making her eat, she thought irritably, but then, in view of the circumstances in which they had met, it probably wasn't surprising. He probably had her down as a dizzy female who went in for fad diets at the drop of a hat. The thought brought her small chin upwards with a cross jerk.

'I'll wait till lunch if that's convenient. I'm not hungry. Do I eat with Juana?'

He looked down at her, his eyes exploring the delicate line of her chin and her small full lips, the wide dark grey eyes with their heavy fringe of lashes and her smooth, creamy skin. 'Are you trying to make me angry, Beth?' His voice was quiet, even conversational.

'No, of course not.' A sudden glow flushed her cheeks.

'Do you usually eat with the family that you are employed by?' he asked slowly, still in the same mild, moderate tone.

'Well, yes . . .' She spoke reluctantly. 'But to be honest I have never been in this situation before, Señor——' She stopped abruptly. The emerald-green gaze dared her to continue. 'Jay,' she corrected hesitantly as the glow moved up to her hairline. 'The other families I've worked for were more . . .' she searched for the right word that would explain her position without seeming demeaning to her past employers '. . . ordinary,' she finished weakly, angry that he was forcing her to explain something she couldn't.

'You are not a house servant, Beth.' His face was strong and harsh and although he didn't raise his voice she knew she had annoyed him. 'You are Mateo's companion, his friend, and as such you are entitled to be treated as one of the family. It is important that he realises that from the beginning. You are to take no nonsense from him or anyone else. Any problems, of any kind, you refer to me. I want you free to concentrate exclusively on Mateo with no distractions or petty complications. Is that clear?'

'Yes, of course.' She looked at him warily. A beam of sunlight glancing through one of the tall, narrow windows in the passageway had highlighted the thin white scar on his dark face, accentuating the impression of hard vitality and cruel ruthlessness that seemed an integral part of his character. 'Does this mean I have a free hand with your nephew?'

A small smile touched his mouth. 'As far as the boy is concerned you will be answerable only to me.'

'I see.' She stared hard at him for a moment. 'Well, Señor...Jay,' she amended hastily as the green glance flashed fire, 'I will try and accommodate your wishes to the letter, but if——'

'No, Beth.' The liquid voice with its heavy accent was molten steel. 'You won't *try*, you will do it.'

The cursory tone fired her quick temper but as she opened her mouth she saw that his gaze had left her face. He took her arm in a firm grip and she had no choice but to accompany him along the corridor and out through the door at the far end. They emerged into the beautiful room of the day before to find a small dark-haired boy sitting swinging impatient legs, his huge brown eyes immediately fixing on Beth's face as he jumped up at their approach. She forced a smile to her face.

'How do you do, Miss Kerri?' The childish treble was polite and very correct. 'I am very pleased to meet you.'

'I'm very pleased to meet you too, Mateo,' Beth smiled gently, 'but I think if we're going to be friends you had better call me Beth, don't you?' She had to fight a strong impulse to gather the small figure into her arms, he looked so...lost.

The dark eyes flashed immediately to the tall, silent man at her side and she noticed the almost imperceptible nod that Jay gave which caused a delighted smile to break out on his nephew's small face. '*Sí*! I mean, yes.' Again that darting glance to his uncle. The poor child was petrified of him!

'I think Beth would like it if we showed her around a little today,' Jay said smoothly as he took one of Mateo's hands in his, 'and then tomorrow she can find out just how much you do *not* know on such boring topics as mathematics and science. Yes?' Mateo nodded warily, obviously recognising the double-edged question, and Beth's heart went out to the motherless child.

By the time the tour of the house and immediate grounds close to the hacienda was completed Beth felt that she knew a little more about her new charge, if not his tall, austere guardian. It was clear that Mateo had a deep and passionate love for both the ranch and the horses. When they entered the magnificent stable block, which was in pristine condition and immaculately clean, Mateo's small serious face lit up from within. He knew each horse and its history without any prompting from his uncle, reciting ancestry and dates with inordinate pride, his little face aglow. She listened patiently to his talk, her eyes soft.

'This is Tabasco.' Mateo was pointing to a beautiful velvet-brown mare heavy with foal. 'She's mine.'

'She's lovely, Mateo.' Beth smiled at the child warmly.

'We've mated her with an excellent stallion, have we not, Gran Jay, and I may be allowed to keep the foal?'

'There were certain stipulations to that agreement.' Jay's voice was quiet but carried a definite warning.

'I will try, really.' The small face that carried a family resemblance to the tall man looking down at it was eager and Beth longed for a kind word from his uncle to take away the painful hope written on the boyish features.

'Maybe.' Jay's voice was hard. 'But will your efforts be good enough?' The mare nuzzled her soft velvet nose into Mateo's hand, taking his attention, and as Beth and Jay strolled a few feet away towards the open doors she glanced at him curiously, masking her anger and dislike.

'What was all that about?' She kept her voice bland.

For a moment she thought he wasn't going to answer her and then he looked down at her from his great height, his cold face broodingly grim. 'Until recently Mateo has had a Spanish tutor here at the ranch. Señor Cupido has been...disappointed with my nephew's work of late and also his attitude has left a lot to be desired. I have made it plain that unless he applies himself better with you over the next few weeks I will not consider making him responsible for the foal.' His voice was as hard as iron and she flushed angrily.

'That's blackmail.' The protest had been involuntary but he froze into stillness by her side, his eyes narrowed and the harsh face dark with anger.

'No, Beth, it is not blackmail,' he bit out through tight lips. 'I have never resorted to that method of persuasion in my life and certainly not with a child. Mateo is a very wealthy young man and much will be required of him in later years. At the moment there is too much of his mother in him for my liking. He is not too young to start facing what he considers unpleasant duties and carrying them through with diligence and dedication. Life is not a game; neither is it a bowl of fruit that one can choose from at leisure.'

'But he is only nine years old!' she said disapprovingly.

'Nevertheless——' the harsh voice was rigid '—until I can trust him to behave as befits a Rojas male certain privileges will not be automatic. My brother and I were not indulged and neither will he be.' His tone was final and uncompromising.

'Your brother and you had each other and a mother and father,' Beth said sharply, her eyes dark with the unfairness of it all. 'How can you be so hard, so unjust to a small boy?'

There was a deep silence for a few seconds before he replied, and then his voice was still quiet and controlled but with a deep menace in its depths that jerked at her nerves more than any ranting and raving. 'This is your first day here and so I will ignore such impertinence, assuming you know no better,' he said arrogantly, his eyes flashing green fire. 'If you value your well-being, Miss Kerri, do not repeat your mistake. I will not tolerate such discourtesy twice.'

He moved back a pace as he spoke and eyed her up and down, his face coldly contemptuous. 'The blood that runs in my veins and that ran in the veins of my brother is pure and unsullied Spanish, unlike that of Mateo. His mother was English and her character left a lot to be desired.' His words were insulting, and she knew he intended them that way. She made no reply, looking at him steadily, willing herself not to falter before his cruelty.

He shrugged his wide, powerful shoulders lightly as he turned away, clicking his fingers sharply to the two huge guard-dogs that were sitting docilely in the sun, waiting for him by the stable doors. The interior was clearly forbidden to them and they knew their place. As he'd like me to know mine, she thought rebelliously as he marched away towards the house without looking at her again, the dogs trotting a pace behind him like well-oiled machines.

'Looks as if you've declared war, girl,' she muttered quietly to herself as she stood half in the bright sunlight, to one side of the massive wooden doors, waiting for Mateo to finish petting his horse. 'Thinks he's a step above the rest of us poor mortals, does he?' She slanted wide grey eyes upwards, looking into the brilliantly blue sky in thoughtful contemplation. Well, the lord and master of the Rojas ranch was in for something of a surprise over the next few months. She'd tread carefully, yes, she would. She was in no hurry to leave Mateo for a start. From what she had seen he was in desperate need of a little human warmth and companionship, and her heart had gone out to the little scrap of humanity who was clearly unloved and unwanted by his nearest and dearest.

She lowered her gaze to the long, sprawling building in the distance, half hidden behind the old fruit trees and flowering bushes. Jay had gone inside, the two dogs just visible by the wide front door where they sat like two splendid, remote statutes.

He wanted war, did he? Well, she was just the girl to deliver. She had vowed when she had left home at seventeen that no man would ever dominate her again, and she was making no exceptions for the arrogant, proud ruler of this small kingdom. He might hold her in derision and contempt now—partly, she suspected, because of her sex and partly because of her English blood—but before she left this place she would leave her mark on it and him. She lifted her small chin determinedly. The gauntlet had been thrown down and she had picked it up. Let battle commence.

CHAPTER THREE

BETH found that she was forced, over the next few weeks, to revise her initial opinion of the youngest member of the Rojas household. A series of small, irritating events, unimportant in themselves but adding up to a disturbing whole, convinced her gradually that Mateo was indeed a peculiarly disturbed and often determinedly naughty little boy.

On the surface he appeared the docile and charming child of the first day, but she had found he was capable of the most bizarre acts of rebellion and pointless defiance, never trying to dodge the inevitable consequences of his actions and almost seeming to invite the censure that fell on to his small head.

Jay, as she had expected, was rarely around to display any interest in his small charge. She had to admit to herself, reluctantly, that his business interests were vast, and together with the heavy responsibilities of his own thriving ranch and that of his late brother's he was often kept working into the small hours in the large, cluttered, predominantly male study that overlooked the pleasant courtyard and Beth's bedroom. Still, she argued to herself militantly, he could make the time for Mateo if he wanted to. She ignored the small voice of honesty that was telling her the man was on his feet from dawn to dusk as it was, often appearing at dinner tired and preoccupied with the thousand and one problems that went hand in hand with such responsibility.

She had noticed that Jay took the child riding each morning without fail and rarely missed reading to him for a few minutes at bedtime unless he was away on a business trip, but often, for weeks on end, that was the only contact uncle and nephew seemed to have.

In spite of Mateo's calculated naughtiness she was finding herself drawn to the small child more and more, often quite uncharacteristically making excuses for him where there were none.

'Why do you call your uncle Gran Jay?' she asked him one evening when she had been at the Rojas ranch for several weeks. She was tucking him up in bed as she spoke, ready for the expected arrival of Jay, and Mateo was looking impossibly angelic, brown curls wet from his bath and huge spaniel eyes drooping with tiredness. She sat beside him and hugged him to her.

'I don't know.' He looked at her in the perplexed way children did when a grown-up asked them an unanswerable question that they considered should never have been asked. 'Why?'

'Oh, nothing,' Beth said lightly as she brushed an errant curl off his high forehead. It had been a particularly trying day, with Mateo seeming to test her patience at every turn. There were times when it almost seemed as though the small boy was intent on bringing trouble down on to his own head, but that was ridiculous, of course. Still... She looked at him sitting meekly in bed in bright blue pyjamas cuddling an old and rather disreputable teddy bear. He must have known she would find the books and papers he had hidden that morning and guess who was responsible. Why did he do things like that? She could understand how it had irritated his previous tutor and angered his uncle but her main feeling was one of heart-wrenching concern.

'It means Big Jay, doesn't it?' she asked as he relaxed against her slowly, and he nodded solemnly, stifling a yawn with his thin little hand. 'It just seems strange that you don't call him Uncle.'

'His mother preferred it that way.' The cool, deep voice behind her made her start and she swung round quickly to find Jay leaning lazily against the open door, his tanned skin and brilliant green eyes thrown into more prominence by the snowy white shirt he was wearing. He looked hard and dangerous and overwhelmingly handsome, and that familiar flicker of excitement that was always lurking ready for his approach sprang into life.

'I'm sorry, I wasn't prying,' she said quietly as a deep red flush stained her fair skin at the quizzical expression on his face. He always made her feel in the wrong!

'Were you not?' It wasn't a question, more of a rebuke at the lie. 'No matter. You can ask what you like, Beth, as long as you are prepared for the answers.' His eyebrows rose sardonically.

'I'll leave you two alone, then.' She kissed Mateo's small upturned face tenderly, her expression hardening as she faced Jay.

'Till dinner.' He inclined his head and then turned to give his full attention to his nephew. She wandered along to her room, intending to have a shower before changing for dinner. This was the time of the day she hated. It wasn't so bad if Jay had guests staying at the hacienda, which he often did—prospective buyers for one of the horses or hopeful owners wishing to mate their stock with the great Rojas name—but when it was just Jay and her seated at the huge dining table with its beautiful silver cutlery and crystal glassware she invariably became nervous and tongue-tied in spite of her disgust at herself. There was something about him—not just his incredible good looks and big, powerful body, but a darkness, a menacing, brooding ruthlessness that always set the fire alarms off all over her body. She couldn't help it and she fought against it but sometimes she left the room feeling as weak as a kitten and she was sure he sensed how she felt. That was the most humiliating thing of all. How she despised his type of man!

She stood under the shower for some time, letting the warm water ease the tenseness out of her body and wash away some of the self-contempt that was always at the back of her mind these days. 'I do not like him and I am *not* attracted to him,' she whispered fiercely as she washed her hair, rubbing her scalp vigorously with angry fingers. Her pale English skin had turned a gentle honey-brown under the warmth of the Mexican sun, and she smoothed a liberal amount of perfumed body lotion on to her arms and legs before getting dressed, her silver-blonde hair falling in a silky bob around her smooth cheeks.

The dress she chose for that evening was pale apricot silk, its sleeveless classic lines moulding to her shape and showing her slender figure off to full advantage. She had regained the weight she had lost before coming to Mexico—Juana's delicious meals would tempt even the most jaded palate—and now her smooth skin glowed with health and she felt better, at least physically, than she had done in months.

She was standing gazing out of the window into the velvet darkness beyond when Jay entered the dining-room, and so she missed the narrowing of his hard, catlike eyes as he took in her slender figure with its cap of blonde hair. By the time she turned to greet him the usual bland politeness was etched on the rugged features, and if his voice was a little thick she didn't notice.

'I gather you had some difficulty today with Mateo?'

She looked at him carefully. She hadn't told him and she was sure that Mateo wouldn't have done. 'Juana overheard you rebuking him.' He answered her un-spoken question coldly. 'You did not intend to tell me?' His attitude immediately ignited a flame of anger.

'There was no need.' She tried to make her voice casual. 'I dealt with the matter as it arose and prefer to forget it.'

'I would like to be informed of any such occurrences in the future,' he said quietly, ignoring her words as though she hadn't spoken. 'Do I take it that today was not an isolated incident?'

'I didn't say that,' she protested quickly—too quickly.

His dark eyebrows rose, the green eyes glacial. 'You *say* very little, Beth. Is it all men that you dislike or just me?' He couldn't bear for a woman not to fall at his feet, then!

'I have no idea what you mean,' she answered coldly, her eyes sparking. This was the first time an attack had been on a personal level, and suddenly the sexual tension between them was so ripe that she could almost taste it.

He looked down at her consideringly in grim silence, the black hair straight against the collar of his shirt and his big shoulders menacingly taut under the thin silk. He looked for all the world like a beautiful and dangerous jungle cat preparing to pounce on its prey, and for the hundredth time since arriving in this foreign land she regretted her decision in leaving the safety of England. 'No?' He smiled sardonically. 'I think you know exactly what I mean.'

He turned from her, his tall body straight and hard. 'Would you prefer wine or a glass of sherry before dinner?'

'Sherry, please.' She stared at the back of his head as he poured the drinks. She mustn't respond to his subtle teasing; it was imperative that she remain cool and distant and betray as little of herself as she could to this man.

She had been lulled into a false sense of security over the last few weeks, thinking he would leave her alone. She should have known better.

'I think it would be advantageous to both of us, and certainly to Mateo, if you could force yourself to communicate with me, Beth.' He handed her the drink as he spoke and his eyes never left her face, watching with grim amusement as the hot colour surged into her cheeks. 'You seemed a little... tense in England, but I thought that would pass. I can understand that there are certain aspects on which we will not agree but as two sensible adults do you not think we can agree to differ? I am not an ogre, whatever you may think to the contrary.'

She glanced up at him defiantly, her eyes dark in her flushed face and her hair a shining halo round her small head. 'You told me your word was law, that you didn't like conflict——'

'*Dios*!' He set his glass of wine down so sharply on the nearby table that most of it spilt out on to the fine damask cloth, spattering the white linen like drops of blood. 'You really are the most impossible female I have ever——' He collected himself with considerable effort, taking a deep breath before he spoke again.

'I like normal conversation, Beth.' The green eyes glittered with cold fire. 'I can even take a little controversy when the occasion justifies it. What I do not like is for you to creep around the hacienda when I am here in a clear effort to avoid talking to me. I wanted a lively companion for my ward, not a shy little mouse that——'

'How dare you?' Beth saw red. 'How dare you accuse me of creeping around? I have never crept around anywhere in my life, I would have you know, and it would take a better man than you to make me! You're the most conceited, supercilious——' It was a few seconds before she realised he was shaking with silent laughter, the harsh face alight with unholy joy. Too late she realised she had done the very thing he had set out to goad her into doing. He was just like her father, playing his little games.

'Now this, I suspect, is the real Beth.' He walked slowly across to her side and touched her hot cheeks with a cool finger. 'This is the girl I glimpsed in England and again on your first day here before you decided to hide behind this oh, so cool façade.' He let his finger lift a lock of pale blonde hair and watched it fall smoothly back into place. She jerked her head aside angrily, visibly shaking, and he took a step backwards as he looked closely at her trembling mouth. 'Who has hurt you, Beth?' His voice was very low with a rich, soft deepness that set a pulse racing madly in her throat. 'A boyfriend, a lover?' There was something in the dark gaze she couldn't fathom but it totally unnerved her.

'No one, there's been no one. I'm perfectly all right...' Her voice trailed away as the flecked green gaze washed over her hot face. She mustn't betray anything of herself to this man.

'I do not believe you.' His accent lent a seductiveness to his voice that was entirely natural. 'A woman as beautiful as you does not have the armour in place so rigidly unless there is something in her past she cannot forget.' She looked up into the handsome face helplessly and for a moment the story that Mateo had related that afternoon about *el tigre*, the dangerous prowling cat that haunted the northern plains, flashed vividly into her brain. The jaguar was patient when it was stalking its prey, patient and infinitely cunning until the moment came when it would have supreme dominance and deadly power. Then it would strike. Without mercy and knowing no fear. She didn't trust this man, especially at this moment when he was displaying such concern and gentleness. *El tigre*.

The appearance of Rosa carrying their first course on a massive silver tray that was almost as large as the little maid herself saved her from the necessity of a reply, and she moved hastily to the table. Jay stayed where he was for one more thoughtful moment and then slowly joined her, coiling his long, lean body easily into his seat with silent animal grace.

'*Gracias*, Rosa.' He inclined his dark head towards the small girl who immediately coloured a bright red. 'Would you like white wine with your meal, Beth?' That was another thing about him—he missed nothing. He had obviously noticed she rarely finished a glass of red wine, preferring the softer white, but such apparent consideration didn't fool her for a minute.

The meal was delicious, as always. The first course consisted of small tortillas, maize pancakes rolled and filled with herbs and meat and served with a thick spicy sauce, followed by Beth's favourite dish since coming to Mexico, the famous *huachinango a la veracruzana*, a delicately flavoured fish served in an aromatic red sauce of garlic, spices and mild chillies. Juana was very proud of her culinary skills and rightly so; she had the happy knack of serving a meal in which each dish complemented the other. Fresh sliced papaya finished the meal, along with coffee which barely resembled the watery drink of England. Here it was brewed for hours with cinnamon and sugar added and after the few days it took to acquire the taste Beth had found no meal was complete without it.

'I would like to talk to you, Beth.' They had eaten the meal in almost total silence and after finishing her coffee she had risen as usual to escape to her room, leaving Jay free to continue working in his study.

'Yes?' She stood, small and slender, her hair shining like white gold in the muted light, looking down at him as he stretched out in his seat with a small sigh, putting his hands lazily behind his head as he stared up into her wary face.

'You did not answer my question earlier, *pequeña,*' he said quietly as he rose abruptly and walked across the room, through the arched doorway and into the large living area beyond, gesturing for her to follow him with an authoritative wave of his hand. She followed slowly. She had been avoiding anything but the most necessary contact with this man for weeks. On hindsight it had been too much to hope that he would not have noticed her reticence.

He waited until she was seated on the edge of one of the velvet upholstered chaise-longues that were scattered round the magnificent room, and then sat opposite her, resuming his previous position with his hands behind his head and his green eyes narrowed. 'It is over three weeks since you came to my home and I have been giving you time to settle in. I trust you are comfortable?'

'Yes, thank you,' she answered primly, her eyes tight on his face. He hadn't asked for her company tonight to talk about whether she was comfortable or not. She wished he hadn't adopted such a relaxed stance; it drew the white silk tight across his broad chest and bunched the muscles in his strong arms, making her even more aware of his arrogant maleness.

'Yes, thank you.' He repeated her words mockingly. 'And do you think this position is to your liking?'

She stared at him silently, disliking his mood. 'I think I can help Mateo, yes,' she said at last when he made no effort to speak. 'He is a very troubled little boy, Jay; there is something that is eating away at him, young as he is.'

'You do not think he is merely wilful, then?' He had straightened as she spoke, all the laughing mockery fading from his hard face.

'No, I don't,' she answered honestly. 'Do you?'

He looked at her for a long moment without replying and then drew his hand across his face in an uncharacteristic gesture of bewilderment. 'I am not sure, Beth. I do not understand this small relation of mine. I look at him sometimes and I see only Alfredo. Other times his mother is there before me.' He looked at her intently. 'She was not a kind woman, Beth, neither was she a good one.' His mouth was hard.

'Perhaps it would help if you looked at Mateo and saw Mateo,' she said quietly, forcing her voice to appear calm in spite of the mad beating of her heart. There was a dead silence and then his eyelids hid his eyes from her gaze.

'Perhaps.' She could read nothing from his voice and his face was non-committal and yet she sensed her comment had reached him. She couldn't bear his cruel coldness to the child.

'He adores you, doesn't he?' He raised his eyes again as she spoke. 'Has he always been like that or just since——?'

'Always.' He interrupted her abruptly, the harsh face suddenly taut. 'Karen did not like it but there was little she could do beyond persuading the infant to address me as "Gran Jay" rather than the more intimate title of "Uncle". It was supposed to be the child's idea—he had a playmate at the time who was also called Jay. Big Jay and little Jay—you understand?'

'Well, that seems reasonable.' She looked at him carefully. 'You may have misunderstood her. You can't be sure——'

'I am sure.' He looked at her coldly. 'It was the sort of petty victory that gave her pleasure. You would care for another coffee?' She stiffened angrily at the abrupt change of subject.

'No, thank you.' Her voice was clipped and cool.

'A brandy, then?' He eyed her unemotionally.

'No, nothing. I'm rather tired actually; I think I'll go to bed——' He interrupted her immediately.

'Not yet.' The rapier-sharp gaze sliced through her as she sank back down into her seat. 'I am still waiting for the courtesy of a reply to my former question.'

She didn't pretend not to understand him but her small chin raised a fraction of an inch in subtle defiance, and her large grey eyes took on the brilliance of polished stone as she held his gaze. 'I am employed as tutor and companion to your nephew, *señor*. That does not give you the right——'

'I do not need anyone to *give* me the right,' he said sharply, his green eyes blazing. 'What I want, I take, and at this moment I wish you to acquaint me with your history to date. That is not too much to ask, is it? Unless you have a deep, dark secret you do not wish to reveal...'

'Don't be ridiculous...' Her voice faltered to a halt as he rose swiftly and moved to sit by her in one easy motion, taking her chin in his large hand and looking deep into her eyes.

'Careful, now.' His murmur was soft but there was steel underneath. 'You will try my patience too far and then I will not be held responsible for my actions.' His hand was burning her skin where it held her flesh lightly and his dark face was so near that she had an overwhelming impulse to raise her hand and trace the silvery line of the scar that glowed white against his tanned skin. Her lips curled in self-disgust and she froze in his hold.

Here it was again, she thought contemptuously, this ruthlessly selfish male quest for total power in action.

'There is nothing to tell.' Her voice was cold.

'Humour me.' The deep growl was an order that she found herself obeying even as she despised herself for her weakness.

'You know most of it from my agency particulars,' she said slowly. 'I am twenty-five years old, I attended university until I was twenty-one and have had three short-term jobs since then as a private tutor. The last one was for twelve months until——' She stopped abruptly. 'Well, you know the rest.'

'And when you are not working? In your free time?'

'I read, I paint a little... Nothing remotely interesting, I assure you.' Her face was a cool barrier he couldn't penetrate.

'You are most obstinate,' he said softly, a blaze of gold gleaming for a moment in the flecked eyes. 'You know the question I ask. Do you have a boyfriend?'

'No.' Her voice was flat. The inevitable male question!

'And in the past? Who is this man who has caused you to be so...aggressive?'

'I'm not aggressive,' she said angrily, jerking away as she spoke. It was a mistake. The softness of her thigh came into brief contact with the hardness of his and she shot away as though she had been burnt. His face registered her reaction for a fleeting second in the tightening of his mouth, but his voice was cool and calm when he spoke.

'I have often wondered at the English expression "to get blood out of a stone",' he said wryly, 'but no more. Now I understand perfectly.' He paused, his gaze moving to her soft mouth. 'You are a very beautiful woman, Beth, but of course you know this.' Here it was, the seduction technique?

There was a brilliant intensity about the green eyes and she found that words were beyond her as her mouth dried and her skin flickered with warmth. She had been right—*el tigre* was a gentle pussycat compared to this hunter. He raised his hand slowly and gently traced the outline of her face and as he drew her towards him she smelt again that fresh lemony fragrance on his tanned, coppery skin.

'Please, don't...'

Even as she spoke he lowered his head to claim her half-open lips and she jolted with the shock of it, with the searing, yearning response that rose immediately to meet the hunger of his mouth. 'Don't!' She flung herself away with an almost desperate gesture and he looked at her lazily as she shrank into the soft corner of the sofa.

'Why so hostile?' he asked huskily, his hand reaching out to touch the silk of her tumbled hair. 'You do not like me, *pequeña*?'

'No. No, I don't.' She barely knew what she was saying as waves of panic washed over her in stinging awareness. She was afraid, desperately afraid, not so much of his kisses but of the alien response of her own body. This man was everything she despised in a male—cold, cruel, the hard vitality and autocratic coolness hiding a dark, brooding ruthlessness that was without mercy. He was dangerous—just how dangerous she hadn't fully realised till now when her treacherous body had reached out to him like a thirsty doe to water.

'I think you do not tell the truth,' he murmured softly, and as he reached for her again she made a little gesture of repudiation against the injustice of male domination.

'No, don't touch me; you disgust me...' In the split-second before the harsh, handsome face closed against her she was aware of his hand moving to touch the scar on his cheek, freezing midway to his face, but then he had risen in one angry movement and the moment to tell him that he had misunderstood her words was lost.

'*Perdóneme*, I apologise.' He stood towering over her, savage derision biting harsh lines into the chiselled features, and then he turned on his heel, walking quickly out of the room without a backward glance, the wide, powerful shoulders rigid and taut.

'Oh, no...' In her distress she whispered the words out loud into the empty room, swaying back and forth slightly in an agony of guilt. He had thought she was referring to his marked face when she had spoken, that she found it repulsive. She remembered the flash of surprised pain in the shocked eyes, swiftly concealed, and groaned softly. It would have been like a slap on the face after her assurance in England that his injury didn't bother her at all. What a mess; what a hopeless mess. This job was getting more complicated and involved every day. Why hadn't he just left her alone? She was here to look after Mateo, that was all. *That was all*.

It was the middle of the night when she awoke to an urgent small hand shaking her shoulder desperately. 'Beth, please, Beth.' Mateo's voice was thick with tears and as she flicked on the lamp at the side of the bed she realised with a start of surprise that it was two o'clock in the morning.

'What is it?' As she sat up the small boy suddenly flung himself wholesale into her arms, breaking into loud, unrestrained sobs that had more than a touch of hysteria about them. 'Mateo?' She held him close as her mind cleared of the last traces of sleep. 'Are you frightened, darling? Have you had a bad dream?'

He drew himself up and leant back to look into her face with something akin to disgust on his face, and in that second he resembled his uncle more than anyone else, the small face supremely proud and touchingly tear-stained.

'A Rojas would not cry about a bad dream, Beth,' he said quietly, rubbing his wet, flushed face with a grubby little paw.

'You're all dirty, Mateo.' She stared at his messy pyjamas in amazement. 'Whatever have you been doing at this time of night?' She hugged him to her, her mind racing.

'It's Tabasco.' His voice broke again and big tears flooded down the grief-stricken small face.

'Your horse? Is something wrong with the foal?'

'She cannot have it. She has been trying and trying all night. Gran Jay has been with her and somehow I knew something was wrong. I went down to the stables because I could not sleep but Gran Jay will not let me stay. He said he would come and tell me when everything is over but he had promised I could be there when she foaled. He had promised, Beth.'

She thought quickly. Obviously Jay was worried that something was seriously wrong and, knowing how devoted Mateo was to the horse, he could hardly have him witnessing the animal's distress. 'Please don't worry, darling.' She searched her mind for a way to reassure him. 'Your uncle loves Tabasco nearly as much as you do. He will look after her. You must trust him; he knows best.' She brushed away an errant teardrop tenderly.

'Grown-ups do not always know best.' The little face was white with worry and streaked with tears and her heart went out to him. 'My mother, she did not love my father any more. This could not have been the best, could it?' He moved away as he spoke.

She looked at him carefully, recognising that in his overwhelming distress and concern for his beloved Tabasco all the usual barriers were down. She had never

heard him mention his parents since she had arrived in
Mexico. 'I'm sure your mother loved your father very
much,' she said gently. 'Sometimes people say untrue
things if they are having an argument or something, and
it's all forgotten the next day. Grown-ups can be just as
silly as children, Mateo, even mothers and fathers.'

'My mother did *not* love my father any more,' he repeated stubbornly, the dark eyes tragic, and suddenly
the small face crumpled and he was weeping in earnest,
giant sobs racking the thin little body as though they
would tear him apart. She held him close for a long time
until he quietened to the odd hiccup, not speaking, just
stroking the damp brown hair off his forehead in slow,
rhythmic comfort. 'May I tell you something, Beth?'

She glanced down at the wet face staring up at her.
'Of course.' She stroked his cheek gently. 'Anything you
like.'

'Will you promise not to tell Gran Jay?'

'I can't do that, Mateo.' She settled him more firmly
on her lap. 'Your uncle loves you and he is responsible
for you. It might be something that he should know.'

'It is not.' The tone was very definite. 'If you told him
he would not give me Tabasco's foal.'

'Mateo?' She moved him slightly to look more closely
at his pale face. 'Your uncle wants you to have the foal,
you know.' He shook his head slowly and eyed her
miserably.

'I do not deserve it, Beth; really, I do not.'

She cuddled him close for a moment and then spoke
gently against the silky curls. 'What's wrong, darling?
There's something, isn't there?'

He opened his mouth to speak and then shut it again,
writhing almost painfully, his face torn with an emotion
that was too old for his tender years. 'You will not hate
me if I tell?'

'I *can* promise you that,' she said firmly. 'Whatever it is, whatever happens, I promise you I'll still be your friend.'

'And you will not leave me?' As she hesitated the small voice became more urgent. 'Please, Beth, you will not? You will stay? Stay until we both go to England and then I will see you there.' She couldn't resist the pleading in his face.

'Yes, I promise, if I can.' She was getting in deeper and deeper and she didn't know how to handle this situation. 'Please, darling, just tell me.'

'When my mother and father died...' He hesitated, his eyes tight on her face.

'Yes?' she encouraged gently.

'My mother was going to take me away from here, away from my father and the ranch.'

'Was she?' Beth could see that he believed every word he was saying and that there was something more that was causing the tortured look in those big eyes. She waited quietly; it wasn't the time to force a confidence.

'She had told me the night before that I was going to have to be brave, that I would not come back here, not till I was a very big boy. I did not want to go, Beth...'

'Of course you didn't,' she said comfortingly. 'This is where you were born. That's quite natural, darling.'

'So I prayed.' His eyes never left her face for a moment; he didn't even blink. 'I prayed that I would be able to stay here, with Tabasco and all the other horses. That I would not have to go.'

'Yes?' She held the small thin hands tight.

'And then the next day there was the accident and Mother and Father were killed, and I did not have to go.' There was real naked horror in the brown eyes. 'I should not have prayed that, should I, Beth?'

'Mateo.' She gathered him into her arms, looking down at his bent head with a surge of fierce affection. 'The accident was nothing to do with your prayers, I promise you, darling. You trust me, don't you?' He nodded slowly. 'Well, then believe me now when I say that your prayers had absolutely nothing to do with the accident.' They stayed quite still, with his arms tight round her waist, for long moments, and in that time a deep love for this tiny piece of humanity was born in her. 'Try and go to sleep now, darling; you can stay here, and later I'll go and see if Tabasco is all right. Yes?' He nodded again, exhausted by the storm of passionate weeping.

She sat by his side until he had fallen into a restless half-sleep, and then, stopping only to pull on her thick fluffy robe and slippers, crept quietly from the room. There was nothing else for it; she would have to go and confront Jay if he was still in the stables and explain what Mateo had said. It was probably all just a child's vivid imagination but it was real enough to Mateo, and until this particular ghost was exorcised the small boy was never going to be completely recovered from his tragic loss. She couldn't afford to wait till morning and run the risk of Mateo closing up again. It must be brought out into the open now, while he was still tender and vulnerable about his horse.

Once outside in the cool, scented air she sped across to the stable block before she lost her nerve. If she thought about what she had to say to him now, especially after the embarrassing scene of a few hours before, she couldn't do it, and so she mustn't think. Overhead the night sky was a thick black velvet blanket in which minute stars twinkled like tiny sparkling diamonds, calm and serene, but as she pushed open the half-closed doors the first thing that met her ears was the laboured groaning of the big mare and the slow, patient crooning of a human voice.

'Jay?' She could barely see in the half-light and stumbled along the central gangway past the other large enclosures until she came to the big closed-in box at the end where Tabasco had been moved to a few days earlier in readiness for her imminent foaling. 'Jay? Are you in there?'

'Stop making such a noise and come in quietly. Do not make any sudden movements and talk softly.' He had given the instructions in the same quiet sing-song voice that had been crooning incessantly as she had made her way towards the box, and she did as he ordered, moving quietly into the enclosure with the minimum of noise and tiptoeing in the dim light to where Jay was standing in the corner, stroking the head of Tabasco in a strong, calming rhythm while she shook and trembled on tottering, straining legs.

'Do you want me to fetch anyone?' It was clear that the mare was having problems but Jay shook his head slowly as she spoke, without taking his steady gaze off the horse.

'I have sent them all away. They were disturbing her with their panic and concern. She is a pure-bred lady, this one; she can read your mind. She must be treated with love and respect—eh, my beautiful brown mare?' He didn't question her sudden appearance at his side and she sensed that all his energy and attention was centred on the beautiful animal in front of him. It was as though their conversation of a few hours ago had never happened.

As Beth's eyes became accustomed to the shadows she realised that his gleaming, pespiring torso was naked from the waist up, and as her eyes were drawn to his tall, powerful body she felt her breath constrict in her throat. The jet-black hairs on his broad chest were tangled and damp and the muscles rippled sensually under his brown skin as he moved. She couldn't believe she was letting a man's body affect her in this way and was just grateful that he noticed nothing. All his concentration was fixed on Tabasco as he willed her along.

She felt that now familiar feeling of self-disgust tremble along her spine but for the life of her she couldn't stop her body responding to his. He was like some magnificent bronze statue come to life there in the semigloom, and his maleness was a live, potent force that had her trembling even as she despised herself for it.

'Come round the other side of her, but gently, gently,' he said softly, still with his eyes fixed on Tabasco. 'Talk to her, Beth, comfort her, reassure her. You understand?' She did as he asked, her mind moving into gear automatically, and after a few moments he reappeared at her side, his right arm covered in blood and mucus.

'There is a big foal in there but it is still alive,' he said quietly. 'I am going to have to help things along.'

'How do you know it's still alive?' she whispered shakily, and he gave one of his rare illuminating smiles as he looked into her troubled eyes.

'It licked me.'

'It licked you?' Her voice was a squeak and delighted amusement flickered for a moment on his dark face.

'*Sí*.'

'Shouldn't you call a vet or something?' She was now involved with the horse's struggle as much as he was.

'Keep calm, Beth, she can read your voice.' He looked quietly at her. 'I have trained as a veterinary. Rest assured she is in good hands.'

Over the next hour she was to learn that he was absolutely right. She was never to forget that fight for the survival of Tabasco's foal, and when it was born, squirming and snorting into Jay's strong, gentle arms, she could have sworn Tabasco turned round and silently thanked him with her big, mournful eyes. It was a huge baby, nearly twice as big as it should have been, but within moments Tabasco seemed to have forgotten her ordeal and was busy licking her new charge from head to foot with complete maternal devotion.

'I thought we were going to lose both of them.' Jay sat down very suddenly on the stable floor and leant back against the panelled wall with a deep sigh. 'Mateo would have been quite devastated to lose his Tabasco. Ring through to the men's quarters and ask one of them to come and attend to mother and son. I have let them sleep long enough.' He suddenly sounded all Rojas again, the gentle tenderness he had displayed with the mare a thing of the past.

When she returned from phoning in the tiny office at one side of the block Beth noticed that he had slipped on the beautiful silk shirt he had been wearing at dinner over the blood and grime coating his body. It would be quite ruined, she thought disconsolately, her mind trying to avoid the main issue.

'Did Mateo send you to see how Tabasco was doing?' He looked at her strangely as they waited for the men to arrive. 'I had to send him away, you understand? There could have been quite a different ending to the night's events.' There was a streak of blood on his cheek and a black stubble darkening his square chin but he had never looked more handsome. The tenderness and understanding he had shown the frightened animal had twisted her heart until she barely recognised herself or her emotions any more. She didn't like it and it frightened her.

'Well, I suggested coming, actually.' She hesitated. 'It can wait till morning if you'd prefer.'

'No, let me hear it now. Am I to be interrogated on my motives for refusing to allow Mateo to stay or do you wish to inform me that you are leaving on the first available plane?' He sighed deeply as he looked into her pale face. 'And please stop looking at me as though I am going to eat you alive, *pequeña*. It has the effect of making me want to do that very thing.'

She flushed scarlet and then paled as his hand came up to touch her face in a light, teasing gesture. 'You are quite safe, Beth. You have made it plain how you feel.'

As the reply formed on her lips the stable doors swung open and three of Jay's big, burly ranch hands came striding down the passageway, stopping short as they noticed her standing by their master's side. Jay fired some sharp orders in rapid Spanish to which the men listened deferentially, and then took her arm in a firm grip, moving her swiftly down the block and out into the fresh morning air. Already the sky was changing to a deep indigo with streaks of amethyst announcing the dawn of a new day.

They walked back to the hacienda in silence and she noticed that he had immediately let go of her arm once they were outside. She glanced at him once or twice, tall and grim at her side, but he didn't speak again until they climbed the steps to the veranda, when he pushed her down into one of the big easy seats with a small sigh. 'Wait there. I will get us both a cup of coffee and then you can tell me what it is you wish to say.'

He was back within minutes, drawing a seat close to hers and stretching out his long legs under the small table he had placed close to her elbow. The flower-scented air surrounded them in intimate silence in the darkness and she gulped deep in her throat as the piercing eyes fixed on her face.

'Well?' He took a long, deep swallow from the steaming cup.

'It's Mateo. He's asleep in my bed at the moment. He came to me very upset about Tabasco.'

'I have explained about that.' He waved an irritated hand, a frown deepening on his brow. 'It was not possible for the boy to stay.'

'No, I don't mean that.' She didn't quite know how to begin. 'It's what came out of his distress that I want to talk to you about. I think subconsciously he's been punishing himself, or making *you* punish him for deliberate naughtiness, because he feels guilty about being here, about his love for the ranch and the horses . . . and you.' She couldn't hide the accusing censure in her voice, and his eyes narrowed slowly.

'I do not understand. Please explain.'

As she related, word for word, her earlier conversation with Mateo, a range of expressions flitted across the dark, handsome face opposite her, and when she finished speaking he was silent for a moment before swearing softly and placing his head in his hands. 'I should have known.' He stood up so abruptly that his chair went skidding across the veranda to land with a crash against the mellow stone of the house. 'How could I have been so stupid, so blind?' He looked at her with savage self-contempt in his narrowed eyes. 'His character changed so much after the accident—the confusion, the bad behaviour for which there was no cause. I should have been able to see the cry for help.'

'Perhaps you were too close to it?' Beth answered slowly. 'You were dealing with your own loss and seeing to Mateo as well as running both ranches. But he has been hurting, Jay, and hurting badly for too long.' Her heart twisted at the thought.

'And you are saying this is my fault? You are right, Beth,' he said grimly as he swept the black hair back from his brow. 'I have been guilty of a grave error of judgement and through it an innocent child has suffered more than was necessary. *Dios*!' He twisted round and banged his fist in impotent rage against the wall of the house.

As she opened her mouth to speak a small, distraught missile launched itself through the open doorway, wrapping skinny arms and legs round Jay's tall body like a baby monkey. 'They are dead, are they not?' Mateo's voice was shrill with fear. 'My Tabasco and her baby? They are dead?'

Jay's brilliant green eyes met Beth's soft grey ones over the head of his nephew and she rose swiftly. This was a time for the two of them to be alone, to bring all the dark shadows into the light of reason.

As she walked into the house she heard Jay's voice begin to speak, softly and gently, and again it had that soothing calmness she had heard in the stables. For such a giant of a man he could be breathtakingly tender, and her heart gave a funny little twist as she remembered his compassion with Tabasco.

She must leave this place soon! As she slipped into bed under the cool cotton covers the thought became a firm, urgent conviction but she didn't dare to try to analyse why. She just knew, with fierce clarity, that she could not, *must not*, stay.

This wild, beautiful, untamed land with its savage contrasts and passionate people was drawing her into its net, and she suddenly felt, in those early hours of dawn when doubts were magnified and demons of fear set loose, that the net could very easily become a noose around her neck.

CHAPTER FOUR

'BETH! *Por favor*, Beth! You must come and see him. He is quite wonderful.' As Mateo's bright, excited voice rang out, jerking her rudely awake to a room filled with white sunlight, Beth glanced blearily at her tiny alarm clock. Eleven o'clock! Her eyes snapped open in startled disbelief. Surely she couldn't have slept that long? 'It is nearly lunchtime, you know.' Mateo's voice was full of childish reproach. 'And I want to show you Firebrand. Will you come?'

'Give me a few minutes to wash and get dressed and then you can show me him.' Beth smiled at the small boy who nodded his agreement as he sped from the room. What a bundle of energy he was going to be today, she thought ruefully as she let the shower water persuade her fully awake, mentally cancelling the lessons she had prepared in advance the day before. The small face had radiated thrilled delight and she had the feeling that the euphoria would last all day long, rendering work impossible. Whatever Jay had said to the boy had seemed to work, anyway, and for that she was supremely grateful.

She spent the next hour giving due homage to Tabasco's bright-eyed, velvet-nosed colt, and as she listened to Mateo's animated chatter and elated laughter she realised, with a sinking heart, that there was no way she could announce to the child that she was leaving him so soon after the ghosts that had been haunting him had been laid to rest. She would have to stay a little longer, at least until he was established in a secure, steady routine

67

with his mind stable and constant. He was a child of the land he had inherited, passionate and emotional, and another disruption in his life at the moment could easily upset his fragile equilibrium again. She sighed softly; she didn't want to leave him and this beautiful land of eternal spring but every instinct was screaming at her to leave, that delay was dangerous. She shook her head gently. What was the matter with her? She was getting as imaginative as Mateo, and *she* was supposed to be helping *him*!

After a light lunch of *caldo de res*, a clear beef soup, with Juana's delicious home-made garlic bread followed by a caramel custard pudding that was Mateo's favourite, they watched the ranch hands exercising the stallions on the racetrack for some time and then Beth allowed Mateo to join Luis and some of the other men in cleaning out the stables and feeding and grooming the horses, thinking that the hard physical exercise would be good for her small charge, who was still full of nervous energy. Juana had informed her at lunch that Jay was over at Mateo's home for the day sorting out some problems that had arisen in the running of the large farm. Since his brother's death Jay had kept a skeleton staff employed in tending the wheat and sugar cane that his brother had decided to grow after being given the land, with one female servant in the ranch house to keep the light, modern building clean. Mateo expressed no interest in his old home at all. All his love and affection was tied up with the stud farm and in the centuries-old hacienda, which he always referred to as *'mi la casa'*—my house.

By evening the manoeuvre had worked and Mateo was asleep on his feet. After a warm bath and a quick snack Beth was just tucking the tired child into bed when firm, hard footsteps sounded outside the door and it was thrust open, Jay's tall figure filling the doorway with dark, vital energy.

'*Cómo estás*, Mateo?' It was the first time she had heard Jay address his nephew in their native tongue; normally he insisted on English, tersely reminding the boy after any lapse of his intended stay in that country.

'I am fine, Gran Jay.' The little voice answered automatically in English. 'I helped feed the horses today and Luis let me groom Toltec. He said I was as good as the men in my work,' he finished proudly.

'I do not doubt it.' Jay crossed to the bed as he spoke, the emerald eyes gleaming as he smiled one of his infrequent smiles that caused Beth's breath to catch in her throat. 'And your governess? How has your governess fared today?' Beth took a step backwards as he drew near, letting her smooth, silky hair fall over her hot face. There was something in his face, a warmth, that was causing her heart to race and the blood pound through her veins as though they were on fire.

'You are all right, Beth, are you not?' Mateo looked up at her with large brown eyes and she smiled as she nodded her answer.

'And you thanked Beth for her assistance in saving Tabasco and the foal?'

Mateo coloured a horrified red as he sat up swiftly, his eyes wide with apology. 'I am sorry, Beth. Please forgive me.' He glanced quickly at his uncle and then back to Beth as he held out a small hand. 'I forgot to thank you and I did mean to. Gran Jay said he could not have saved them without you.'

'I think that's a slight exaggeration,' Beth said comfortingly as she kissed him warmly before pushing him back down in bed and drawing the cotton covers under his chin. 'I didn't really do anything. Your uncle did it all.'

'I think we will cease in this mutual admiration society.' Jay's deep, rich voice was shaking with restrained amusement. 'You are in Beth's debt, Mateo. You understand?' The small boy nodded slowly, looking more subdued than he had all day. 'And the little one? Firebrand? He is well?' The name was a magic key to release a torrent of words, and Beth left them to it, walking quickly to her room where she sat down on the bed heavily, her legs shaking. This was absolutely ridiculous. She must pull herself together. He hadn't said two words to her and here she was with what could only be described as an attack of the vapours! And to upbraid Mateo like that! The man was as cold as ice.

She looked at her reflection in the large ornate mirror. Her skin was flushed with a pink bloom, her dark eyes bright with a soft light and her mouth parted as though the full lips were waiting to be kissed. She shook herself angrily and rose jerkily to change for dinner. Enough was enough. She was supposed to free Mateo of his fanciful notions, not invent ones for herself.

By the time she entered the dining-room half an hour later she was the epitome of the cool English woman, dressed quietly and discreetly in pale grey silk, her hair brushed into shining sleekness and just a touch of make-up on her smooth skin. The hard-won aplomb faltered briefly when Jay strode into the dimly lit room a moment later. He had added a black silk embroidered waistcoat to his usual evening attire of black trousers and white full-sleeved shirt which accentuated the wide powerful shoulders and hard chest, and increased still further the overall impression of a wild and dangerous *caballero*. A shiver raced down her spine but she forced her eyes to remain steady and calm as they met his piercing stare.

'Champagne tonight, I think.' The dark voice was laughing at her; she could feel it. He knew he unnerved her.

'Champagne?' The squeak irritated her still further and she cleared her throat and tried again. 'Are we celebrating something?'

'But of course,' he said softly, his green eyes glowing with that cold fire that lit the darkness of his skin like an internal lamp. 'We have much to rejoice in, do we not?'

'We do?' For goodness' sake stop it, Beth, she thought angrily. You sound like his echo. He'd just love that.

'You have seen the change in Mateo today? The way the burden has been lifted from his shoulders?' She nodded slowly. 'That is all due to you, Beth. I cannot adequately express my thanks to you.' All amusement had fled the sombre voice and his gaze was warm on her flushed face. 'I have been guilty of a great injustice to my nephew but this I will discuss with you later. For now, a glass of champagne and then we eat. *Sí*?'

'Yes. Thank you.' She faced him squarely, unable to forgive the months of indifference to Mateo immediately. 'All children should be carefree and happy and he is thrilled you saved Tabasco and her foal.' Somehow she couldn't accept his thanks, his gratitude.

'So I did.' His voice was quiet and she risked a quick glance at him to find an expression of thoughtful speculation on the austere features. 'But again you helped me.'

'Really, I didn't do anything...' She wanted the conversation finished and her voice was cool.

'Beth... Beth.' He shook his head slowly as he lifted the opened bottle of champagne from the ice-bucket and poured two sparkling glasses, walking across to hand her hers with a wry grimace. 'Why do you find it dif-

ficult to acknowledge my appreciation? Is even such a
slight intimacy repugnant to you?'

She looked at him with wide eyes as he held on to the
glass when she tried to take it from him, causing their
hands to be joined by the gleaming crystal. She knew
she should make some light, throw-away comment to
alleviate the sudden tension but her mind had refused
to function as he reached her side, his big, broad body
towering over her and making her feel painfully
vulnerable.

'Such a little thing and yet so fierce.' His voice was a
caress in itself and for the life of her she couldn't have
moved or spoken. 'Why so defensive, so unfriendly?'

She stared at him for a full minute as their eyes locked
and held, and then as he released the glass and took a
sip from his own, his eyes never leaving her face, she
found the strength to lower her head and drink herself.
'I'm not little.' She ignored the rest of his words. 'It's
just that you are so tall.' And cold, and hard, her mind
added silently.

'Ah, too tall?' There was that throb of laughter in his
voice again and a sharp little pang, of anger, of hurt,
turned her eyes black and stopped the trembling in her
legs. This was all just a game to him, an amusing dis-
traction. He was clearly the type of man who couldn't
bear to be defied, even a little. She had gained his interest
when she had dared to challenge his authority and he
wouldn't rest until she was like everyone else round
here—scared stiff of him and subservient.

'I think so.' She raised her eyes and the light in his
face died at the expression on hers. How could she have
been so stupid, so foolish, as to forget all the lessons she
had learnt in the first half of her life? You didn't give
an inch, displayed no weakness, because if you did it
would be quickly capitalised on. She would never let

herself come under the domination of another man in her life. Her mind, her will was her own. This physical attraction was less than nothing.

'Then it must be so,' he said softly, and for a terrifying moment it was as though he had turned everything around, had won the battle without a shot being fired. She finished her glass of champagne without realising what she was doing and he glanced at the empty glass wryly. 'I seem to have discovered a beverage which you enjoy. We will have to have champagne every evening, *si*?'

'I was thirsty.' Her voice was defiant.

'Of course,' he agreed smoothly.

The arrival of Juana and Rosa with the food stopped further conversation, but she noticed the musing contemplation on his dark face more than once during the meal as his gaze scanned her face. She forced herself to eat with every appearance of enjoyment but for once the excellent food tasted like sawdust in her mouth. Somehow, imperceptibly, their relationship seemed to have altered, and she didn't like it. She didn't like it at all. She needed to keep every part of her mind hidden from this hard, powerful man but her feelings kept getting in the way.

'I would be grateful if you would take a walk with me, *pequeña*,' Jay drawled as they finished coffee. 'There are certain matters I must explain to you if you are to understand Mateo better.'

'*Pequeña*? That means small one, doesn't it? I wish you wouldn't call me that,' she said irritably as she rose abruptly, flinging her linen napkin down on the table with a slight toss of her head. How could he explain his treatment of the boy?

'I apologise, Beth.' His voice was liquid cream but as she glanced at him she saw that his narrowed eyes were cold and for a moment a little dart of fear swept through her.

Why did she do it? Why keep irritating him? Mateo needed her here and his uncle was quite capable of sending her home on a whim. She was being uncharacteristically rude and she liked it as little as he clearly did. 'I'm behaving badly, I'm very tired.'

'You will need a covering for your arms. The night air is a little cool tonight.' He had accepted her apology with a cool nod but she knew instinctively that the weak excuse hadn't fooled him.

He was waiting for her on the veranda when she returned from collecting a cardigan, leaning lazily against a wooden pillar and sipping another glass of champagne. 'All ready?' he asked pleasantly as she joined him, and she nodded silently. She didn't want to go for a walk with him. If there was anything in life she didn't want at this moment in time it was that.

He didn't speak as they wandered through the small orchard and round to the side of the hacienda where the quiet landscaped gardens began. She had been overwhelmed when she had first explored them some weeks before with Mateo. In the day they had been a blaze of colour that had stretched on and on, and although she didn't know most of the trees, shrubs and flowers she could appreciate how perfectly they had been planned to complement each other, the occasional fountain and small, secluded bower adding to the enchantment.

'My grandfather designed all this right down to the last shrub,' Jay said after a while as they strolled slowly down one winding path, the heavy perfume of honeysuckle, jasmin and the lemon-scented verbenas rich on the night air. 'I saw the blueprint once. It was more complicated than any building.'

'It's absolutely magnificent, though. Your grandmother must have been thrilled,' she said quietly.

'I do not think it was intended for that purpose.' His voice was very dry. 'My grandfather had decided to have a garden similar to the one he remembered as a child in his home in Spain, and therefore everything had to be perfect and of the best quality. My grandfather was a very proud and cold man. I do not think he would even have thought to consider my grandmother's wishes.'

'Oh.' Her voice was thoughtful. So that was who he took after?

'He was also very cruel but fortunately my father inherited none of his callousness, merely his great love of the horses, which possibly did not make him a good businessman but certainly an excellent father. You see me in the same mode as my grandfather?' It was termed as a question but Beth realised that it was more of a statement, and one she couldn't in all honesty deny.

She shrugged slowly. 'I don't know you . . .' Her voice died away as she glanced up at him by her side to see him looking down at her with a quizzical expression on his watchful face.

'No, you do not,' he agreed softly, 'and you intend to make sure that eventuality does not come about. What exactly is it, Beth? Does this trouble you so much?' He touched his face with a quick gesture. 'I do not somehow see this as true and yet you leave me no choice but to assume so. And yet . . .' He stopped and turned to face her, forcing her to stand still too. 'I wonder?' His voice was thick and deep and she gulped desperately in her throat. He was devastatingly handsome there in the moonlight, the soft light from the small ornate lamps along the path giving his darkness a mysterious allure and accentuating his powerful, wide shoulders and sensual features. 'For someone who is so fierce you are so timid, little one. I do not understand you at all.'

She knew he was going to kiss her but was powerless to move, and as his firm, hard lips touched hers in a light kiss that merely brushed hers she shivered helplessly, sensing the iron control that was holding the big, tall body taut. 'Who has frightened you so badly, Beth? What has happened to make you flinch from me every time we meet?'

'Please... I can't. There's nothing. Nothing's happened.' She took a step backwards as she spoke and lowered her head so that a cloud of silver silk hid her face from his glittering eyes. She heard him draw his breath in a harsh gasp and then there was quiet, with just the sound of a running fountain near by breaking the stillness. 'You said you wanted to talk about Mateo? That you needed to explain things? That is why we came out.' She could hear the note of fear in her voice herself, so he must be able to. She shut her eyes for a second in humiliation. He must think her an utter fool, and this was all his fault!

'Yes. Mateo.' She felt him begin to walk again and raised her eyes to see him slowly moving away, his hands thrust in the pockets of his trousers and his face turned from her. 'Please treat the matters I confide to you in strict confidence, Beth.' The quiet voice was deep and calm with not a tremor betraying the passion she had seen in those green eyes a moment before. She looked at his back in bewildered confusion. She had expected him to press his advantage; he had seen her trembling, sensed her helplessness, and instead he was giving her time to collect herself. It didn't match the picture she had of him at all. And yet? Her mind was racing. *El tigre* was cunning. Cunning and shrewd. It always waited until it was sure of its prey, biding its time.

'Unfortunately Karen never settled in this country. She met my brother when he was on holiday in England and for Alfredo it was love at first sight. He had had other women, of course, but there was something about Mateo's mother that captivated him.' From the harsh note in his voice Beth assumed that Jay could not understand why. 'She appreciated his wealth and good looks and within six weeks he had married her. Against all advice and counsel. He lived to regret it.' The deep voice was cold with hate. 'She was a tramp and she made his life hell. Any man, any time, would do. Even the ranchhands——' He broke off abruptly and Beth was glad that she was a step behind him and couldn't see his face. Surely he was exaggerating?

'The disgrace broke my father's heart. He died three years after Alfredo brought her to his home and I decided that she must be sent away—how you say, bought off? Her interest in Mateo was spasmodic. When she was conducting an affair she would forget the child existed for weeks on end and then when it ended, as it invariably did, she would spoil the boy unmercifully. I made arrangements but...' He paused. 'Would you care to sit down?' He indicated a low wooden seat to one side of the path and she sank down quietly after one glance at his hard face, his mouth a thin white line. 'My brother did not want her to go.' There was a note of incredulity in his voice.

'He thought that maybe if she had her own home then she would behave like a wife and mother. I loved my brother.' He leant forward where he was standing with both hands pressed against a small stone wall overlooking a rose garden and looked across the scented darkness, his profile savage. 'But he was foolish, foolish and weak, and she destroyed him. I built them a home but she was rarely in it; she treated him with no respect

because in the end he deserved none. He should have
whipped her to within an inch of her life at the first
infidelity, brought her to heel.'

Beth stiffened in outrage at the brutality of his words,
but then, she reasoned angrily, she might have guessed
he would use force as the answer! There was no doubt
that he meant every word he had said as he ran a hand
through his dark hair before moving to sit beside her,
his long legs outstretched. She wanted to move away but
kept still.

'I was at their home on the day of the accident discussing business with Alfredo. One of the ranch-hands
came in to say he had seen Karen loading some suitcases
into her car with Mateo quite hysterical in the back. She
had been going to leave without a word.' The slanted
eyes were as cold as ice. 'When Alfredo confronted her
she told him she was leaving for Guadalajara. There was
a man there.' His lips curled in disgust. 'There was the
inevitable scene and as she left Alfredo jumped in the
car. She was driving like a mad woman, quite out of
control. The rest you know.' He shrugged his big
shoulders slowly. 'I shall never know exactly what was
said in those minutes before the crash; it seems blanked
out of Mateo's memory, mercifully so.'

'Thank you for telling me; it will help me understand
Mateo better,' Beth said stiffly, sensing that the revel-
ations had been both embarrassing and painful, doubly
so with his sense of family pride and history.

'I am glad Mateo resembles Alfredo but I confess I
have been watching him, waiting to see his mother's bad
blood make itself known. The perverse behaviour was
confirmation of all I feared. I did not seek to understand, to assist him. I added to his confusion.'

Beth couldn't bring herself to offer false comfort.

'But Mateo is a person in his own right. You said yourself that your father did not resemble his father,' she said indignantly.

He looked at her tightly, his Spanish heritage very obvious. 'But my grandmother did not have pale skin and golden hair and men were safe with her. There is a difference, Beth.'

His words affected her like a slap in the face and the reaction must have shown in her eyes, because his expression changed suddenly as his hand reached out to her. 'Do not misunderstand me, Beth. I did not mean——'

'It doesn't matter.' She rose so swiftly to escape his touch that she almost fell, her voice cool. 'Your opinion on women doesn't affect me one way or the other, does it? I am here merely to do a job and I can assure you that I will do it to the best of my ability for Mateo's sake.'

'He is already very fond of you.' Jay didn't comment on her words but his face had hardened into its usual austere lines.

'Children know when they are loved.' She hadn't meant it as further condemnation but saw that he had taken it as such by the darkening of his face. Well, she thought defiantly, if the cap fits—wear it.

They walked in mutual silence as they retraced their steps to the brighter lights beyond and she kept her face bland and her chin high. He mustn't suspect for a moment that his words had affected her at all but they were burning into her brain and she couldn't understand why. She didn't even like him, despised and detested him in fact, so why worry about his view on English women? Pale skin and golden hair. Her chin went a shade higher. There was no way she was going to apologise for the way she looked!

'I need to check on Tabasco and the foal before bed. Would you like to see Firebrand again?' His voice was expressionless as though he didn't care one way or the other, and that fact alone made her agree instantly. This was one woman who wouldn't creep from his presence like a whipped dog!

'Fine.' She knew he was looking at her but kept her gaze straight ahead. 'He's a sweet little thing.'

There was a dim light burning in the stables when they reached the quiet building, and most of the horses were asleep, one or two of the big animals opening beautiful brown eyes and attempting to nuzzle Jay's body as he passed. Tabasco's foal was feeding, pressed into its mother's side, and the sweet scent of fresh hay and clean straw reached Beth's nostrils as she watched, enchanted, unexpectedly enthralled.

'I cannot think of a more exquisite sight. Unless, perhaps, a woman feeding her baby.' Jay's voice was soft beside her and almost absent-mindedly he took her hand and drew it through his arm. 'Come. It is late and you are tired.'

It would have seemed churlish to withdraw her hand after what seemed a purely friendly gesture, but his action had brought her close to his side as they began to walk and she was breathlessly conscious of his hard-muscled body in the dim half-light.

'You were kind to Tabasco last night. A kindness, I think, that is natural.' The bright moonlight threw his features in sharp shadows as they came out of the dim light in the stables, and she saw that his face was sombre. She had an overwhelming desire to reach up and touch his cheek and the impulse shocked her to the core. She didn't understand how she could thoroughly dislike a man and yet feel an attraction so strong that it was a physical ache.

'She was frightened,' she answered flatly.

'And you sympathised with her, understood her?' He was asking more than the mere words said and now she did draw her arm from his, lowering her head and concentrating on her steps.

'Yes, I understood her. We've all been frightened at times, haven't we? Different causes maybe, but the feeling is still the same.' She kept her voice calm and steady. Maybe this hard, dark master of the Rojas empire had never known a moment's fear in his life. She could believe that was so. He wasn't like other people, other men.

'And you think I am incapable of such an emotion?' His perception unnerved her. He seemed to read her mind as easily as though it were an open book.

'I didn't say that,' she answered stiffly, hackles rising.

'No, Beth. That is true. You did not *say* it.' He stopped and turned her round to face him, his hands warm on her shoulders through the thin cotton. 'But that is the thought that was in here.' He tapped her head gently and then stepped back a pace, his dark face quizzical. 'You are a puzzle, little one.'

He started walking again and she fell into step by his side. 'I have known fear,' he said quietly, looking straight ahead towards the lights of the house, his hands thrust into his pockets. 'It can cause the heart to race and the adrenalin to pump and for that reason I have much to be grateful for. But for that little hormone secreting its fierceness into my blood I would never have got Mateo free from the wreckage in time.' She looked at him sharply and then lowered her eyes again swiftly. There was a wealth of sadness in the harsh lines of his face and somehow it hurt her to see it.

'Unfortunately it was not enough to save my brother, but then maybe he would not have wanted to live without

his Karen.' He looked down at her blonde head broodingly. 'There is a time to be born and a time to die, and
maybe that was his time. Who knows?'

'Do you really believe that?' she asked quietly, and
jumped as he swung round to face her fully, his face
dark and haunted and his green eyes flashing sparks.

'No, I do not believe it, but what would you have me
do, my critical little English rose? Weep and wail and
wear sackcloth and ashes? I have no time for such in-
dulgences. I have two ranches to run as well as my other
business interests, and a young child who is dependent
on me for some degree of stability in his life. His mother
was a slut who contaminated the very air around her,
and his father...' He paused. 'His father was weak and
spineless. Is that how you like your men, Beth, grovelling
on the ground?'

'No...' She took a step backwards but he whipped
her against him, his hands hard and rough.

'But all the time you look at me with those big grey
eyes and there is distaste in their depths.' She jerked
against his hold.

'You're hurting me,' she said coldly. 'Please,
Jay——'

'Please? Please?' His eyes were glacial. 'What is it
you ask for, Beth? Is it this?' His lips captured hers in
a hard, cruel kiss that bent her head backwards and
forced her to clutch at him for support. For a moment
she was too surprised to struggle and then reaction set
in and she twisted in the iron arms violently, trying to
force her head away from his. It was like being held by
a body of steel and she made no impact on the rigid
frame with either her fists or her feet. In fact, as she
writhed and twisted, he pulled her even closer, sliding
one hand under her neck to support her head while he

plundered her lips, and the other hand he curved round her back in a vice-like hold.

As he forced her lips apart the shock of her first intimate kiss caused sheer panic to race through her veins, but then as she began to tire and weaken she couldn't deny the tiny flickers of excitement and desire that shivered up her spine. She felt like a tiny trapped creature that was being forced to recognise that its life was no longer its own, and along with the desperation a gasp of unbidden pleasure had her breathless as the kiss began to change subtly into a coaxing, provocative caress. Even in her innocence she recognised his skill and experience but somehow she couldn't summon up the will to resist him.

His lips began to trace a trail of fire all over her face, over her closed eyelids, across her cheek and down to where a small pulse was beating frantically in her throat. She heard a voice moaning softly and with a thrill of horror realised it was her own, but even as she stiffened her whole body began to tingle helplessly. Moulded against him as she was, she couldn't fail to feel the evidence of his desire, and even though the power of his male body frightened her with its alien passion something deep inside her was responding to the age-old call almost against her will.

'So small and so perfect...' His voice was thick and husky against her lips and as his hands ran over her back in a burning caress she felt herself pushing deeper into his big body, drinking in the feel and smell of him in tiny gasping sobs. His hands ran down the length of her, stopping at her hips and drawing her fiercely against his thighs as his kiss became even deeper.

'Beth...Beth...' His voice was shaking and as he moved her from him in one violent movement of rejection she couldn't believe for a moment that she was free, that he had really let her go.

'Jay?' Her voice was a tiny whisper but he heard it and groaned deep in his throat as he turned away from her, looking out over the darkness like a huge rigid statue, his head high.

'Go back to the hacienda, Beth, now!' His voice was tight and cold and she almost whimpered with pain, but couldn't move, standing like a pale, slender shadow in the moonlight with her eyes full of shocked surprise. This couldn't really be happening, not to her. It was like a bad dream.

'I mean it, Beth, leave now.' There was savagery in his voice. 'Or do you wish me to take you here, on the ground, like a common whore?'

The harsh word jolted her out of the stillness that seemed to have taken hold of her mind and body, and she backed from him with wide eyes, turning and running wildly towards the distant house on trembling legs that threatened to let her down with every step.

How could she have betrayed herself so completely? As she reached the safety of her room she collapsed on the bed in an agony of weeping, his last words ringing in her ears with terrible condemnation. All her self-esteem, her pride lay in tiny fragments around her. He would think she was just like Karen, available and willing for any man who wanted her, with the morals of an alley cat. She groaned and twisted on the bed, seeking relief from the torment in her mind. How could she have behaved so wantonly, so stupidly?

After a time a semblance of calmness quietened her and she lay, spent and unmoving, on the soft bed as her bruised mind dulled. How he must be laughing at her! Even that thought didn't have the power to raise her from the lethargy that seemed to have taken possession

of her senses. He was experienced enough to know—
and his words had confirmed it—that she had been his
for the taking. What he didn't know was that the whole
situation had come about because of her complete innocence, her gullibility. She had never dreamt that a man's
kisses could make her feel like that.

And he hadn't wanted her! She sat up suddenly as her
mouth hardened and her mind cleared. Well, that suited
her just fine. She wasn't going to run away, like a small
animal that had been ill-treated by its owner. She
wouldn't let him win. She had been right all along; he
had just been seeking a way to bring her under his
control.

'You won't beat me, Señor de Rojas,' she whispered
into the silent room. 'I'll stay here for as long as it suits
me to stay and I'll leave when *I* want to leave, but in the
meantime I shall behave as I see fit.' She looked at the
wall in front of her with unseeing eyes. She would act
as though nothing had happened between them tomorrow, as indeed it hadn't really. She gave a short,
sharp bounce with her head. In this day and age what
were a few kisses after all, a heated embrace? It was
nothing, nothing. She nodded again. But how she hated
him!

CHAPTER FIVE

'GRAN JAY is home tomorrow, Beth.' Mateo's voice was sleepy but full of anticipated delight. 'Do you think he may bring me a present?'

'You'll have to wait and see.' Beth smiled lovingly at the small boy as she tucked him up in bed, amazed as always at the forgiving power of children. Jay had been severe with his nephew with a hardness bordering on cruelty, and yet, since the night of Firebrand's birth and the change of attitude by his uncle, in Mateo's eyes the previous years were all swept away. She wished she could be as magnanimous but the more she grew to love her small charge the more her heart wept for the lost months. And she did love him! Her eyes clouded as she looked at the little face topped by the mass of silky curls. Too much. The thought of leaving him was getting more and more painful. But, as Mateo had just reminded her, his uncle would be home tomorrow.

After the night when Jay had made such passionate love to her she hadn't seen him again. She had learnt the next morning from Juana that he had been called away to America on urgent business connected with the stud farm and had apparently left early that morning before daybreak. At first she had been glad of the reprieve but as the days had dragged on into weeks the inevitable meeting had assumed momentous importance and she had been sleeping badly.

'I am so glad you came to live with me, Beth.' Mateo looked up at her, his huge brown eyes soft with affection. 'Everything has been so nice since you arrived.'

'Has it? Good.' Beth sat down on the bed and cuddled the thin little body close. 'It's been nice for me too, to be with you.'

'You won't leave, will you? Not ever.' The childish voice held a note of fear and she stroked his forehead gently as she replied.

'Ever is a long time, darling, but it seems to me you still have plenty of work to catch up on to keep us both busy.'

'Good.' Mateo turned over and tucked his battered old teddy bear under his arm in preparation for sleep. 'I will learn very, very slowly and then you will still be here when I am grown-up.' He suddenly sounded exactly like Jay. 'Then I shall marry you and you will never leave the Rojas ranch.' There was a note of almost adult determination in his voice.

Beth forced the flutter of panic the childish words had caused to quieten. It was only a young boy's dreams. Of course she would leave the ranch. She was free to leave at any time. Only her love for Mateo was keeping her at the moment.

'Well, you'll be in charge of your own farm when you are grown up, won't you?' she said quietly as she walked towards the door. 'So we will have to live there, won't we?' The teasing note in her voice was quite lost on Mateo.

'Maybe.' The word was muffled by the cotton sheet. 'I may decide to join with Gran Jay. I asked him if I could the night Tabasco's foal was born and he said we would sort it out in the future.'

'Well, that's all a long way away, Mateo, and it's sleep for now. I'll see you in the morning, darling.' She shut the door and stood for a minute in the corridor, wondering why the child's words had unsettled her. She was getting as jumpy as a cricket and it would have to stop.

She'd feel better when she had seen Jay again and got that particular hurdle over and done with.

She strolled along to her room and had a leisurely shower, washing her hair under the warm water and towelling it dry with one of the huge fluffy bath-sheets. Since Jay had left she had asked Juana to serve her evening meal on a tray and little Rosa would be bringing it along in a few minutes. Tonight it seemed too much effort to dress again and so she merely slipped on a thin cotton nightie and one of the thick towelling robes that were provided fresh each day. There was something to be said for living in such luxury, she thought idly as she brushed her hair until it shone like liquid silk. It was going to be hard to get used to cooking her own meals again and doing her own laundry.

The expected knock at the door announced Rosa's arrival with the meal, and after calling for her to enter she didn't look up for a moment, creaming body lotion into her smooth skin with concentrated effort. It was the tingling sensation in her spine that caused her to glance up after a second as some sixth sense warned her of danger.

'*Buenas tardes*, Beth.' Jay stood leaning in the open doorway, his eyes bright and glittering in the darkness of his tanned skin.

Oh, help, Beth breathed silently. She had forgotten how devastatingly handsome he was and the shock of seeing him again, unexpectedly and without warning, momentarily robbed her of speech. She hadn't had time to marshal her defences.

'You are well?' His glance flickered over her night attire and she flushed scarlet as she pulled the thick robe more closely round her, knotting the belt with a tight little jerk that betrayed her agitation to the piercing eyes watching her every move. How dared he creep into her room? She ignored the knock.

'I'm fine, thank you,' she answered stiffly. 'Just a little tired so I thought I would have an early night. You weren't expected home until tomorrow.'

'That is correct.' He didn't move from the doorway and for a moment Beth had the feeling that he was as embarrassed as she was, but of course that was absolutely ridiculous. 'There was an unexpected vacancy on an earlier flight and so I took it. The business was concluded satisfactorily and so there was no need for me to stay.' The green eyes moved over her face and down her body to where her legs, long and bare, showed beneath the short robe. 'I wanted to return home.'

'Yes, of course.' She lowered her eyes from his face with considerable effort and concentrated furiously on a spot on the wall to the left of him. 'There's nothing like one's own bed, is there?' What an inane remark, she thought angrily.

'Indeed there is not.' She just knew it was suppressed laughter causing that slight tremor in his deep voice, and as she raised her eyes to his face again she saw that his eyes were full of mocking amusement. 'Can I persuade you to dress and join me for dinner?'

'I'd rather not, if you don't mind.' She brushed back her silky hair with a hand that shook slightly. 'I really am very tired and I've a headache.' How dared he laugh at her?

'That is a pity.' The smooth voice showed no emotion. 'I will ask Juana to place some medication on your dinner tray. Mateo? He is well?' His cold face was expressionless now.

'Mateo's fine. He's been longing for you to come home. I think he is expecting a present.' She tried for lightness.

The dark face relaxed as his firm lips twitched in a small smile. 'He will not be disappointed. I normally bring the child something from my travels.'

'Oh, good.' Her heart was pounding so hard that she was sure he would hear it, and that familiar feeling compounded of fascination, rebelliousness and anger was causing the pink to remain in her cheeks. Why couldn't she be cool and offhand like him? Why did her traitorous body long to fling itself into his arms and offer a welcome in which words played no part? She hated herself for her weakness and she hated him still more.

'Sleep well, Beth.' He turned from her as he spoke and the next moment the door was closed with a firm click and she was left, staring open-mouthed at its blankness. Just like that! He could leave her just like that! She didn't affect him at all.

The following days resumed the routine that had been customary until Jay's trip: lessons with Mateo in the morning until lunch at one-thirty p.m., after which the small boy was allowed to choose a couple of hours of relaxation, which inevitably meant time with the new foal and his mother. Then more schoolwork until six o'clock when Mateo had his evening meal followed by bath and bed. As before, Beth found the next hour or two in Jay's company a strain and was always glad to escape to the safety of her room after the meal was finished.

She couldn't quite fathom Jay's attitude at the moment. Apart from the night he had returned home he had made no effort to see her alone or even talk to her beyond the bland day-to-day conversation in the evening, normally enquiring after Mateo's progress and discussing small instances that had occurred in the course of the day. It was almost as though he was biding his time, treading warily, but Beth dismissed such thoughts as over-active imagination on her part, along with the impression she had at times that he was holding himself in some sort of iron control.

One or two business contacts connected with the stud farm came and went but otherwise the routine remained the same, and as the days rolled by in easy familiarity Beth found herself beginning to relax and question Jay's motives more kindly. Perhaps the night after Tabasco's foaling had been a purely impulsive gesture on his part, something he had immediately regretted and was determined to forget. It irked her a little but she was honest enough to admit that she could have made a mistake. Maybe she had wronged him in assuming his actions had been born of a desire to subjugate her and 'bring her to heel'. The words he had used to describe how he would have treated Karen were always there at the back of her mind.

She was in this mellow frame of mind one golden, sunny afternoon as she sat idly on a huge bale of hay in the stables watching Mateo groom Tabasco. Firebrand was in a playful mood, nuzzling against Mateo's legs as he worked to make the big mare's coat shine, and pushing his velvet nose under the boy's arm when the opportunity presented itself. The small colt seemed to realise he was the star of the show and never missed an opportunity to show off. She giggled delightedly as a particularly vigorous nudge sent Mateo sprawling in the straw, and then froze as a deep male voice drawled lazily beside her.

'You should do that more often, *pequeña*, it suits you.' She spun round so hastily that she nearly toppled from her seat, to find Jay's sea-green eyes fixed tightly on her face.

'You startled me,' she accused breathlessly.

'I apologise.' He was wearing the usual full-sleeved white shirt, buttoned at the cuffs and open at the throat just enough to show a glimpse of his hair-roughened chest. She remembered how his powerfully muscled body had gleamed in the dim light on the night Firebrand was born, and gulped in her throat. It was a particularly muggy afternoon and, dazed by his sudden arrival, she spoke without thinking.

'There's no air, is there? I'm surprised you aren't galloping across the plain on Tornado.' Tornado was Jay's huge black stallion and, as his name suggested, wild and untamed. Jay was the only one who could ride him, and all the ranch hands held the unpredictable animal with a mixture of respect and awe coupled with healthy dislike.

Whenever Jay was away from the ranch the men drew lots on who was to let the huge beast into the exercising compound, and she had seen even the biggest of them turn a shade paler when he drew the short straw.

'I have been busy,' he answered lightly, 'but maybe you would care to accompany me on an afternoon ride? Come and see Tornado. He is restless now he has heard my voice.' She took his proffered hand because there was no way she could refuse, quickly letting go as soon as her feet touched the ground. His touch did the weirdest things to her insides and she could feel his warm flesh against hers long after he had moved away. It was as irritating as it was unsettling.

'Hello, my old friend.' As they reached Tornado's massive enclosure the horse whinnied softly at Jay's voice before rolling his black eyes at Beth in the background. 'Do not be nervous of him. He knows exactly what it is you are thinking.' Jay glanced behind him, reading the apprehension in Beth's face accurately. 'He is the best and he knows it.'

Like master, like horse, Beth thought wryly.

'Come here, *pequeña*.' He beckoned imperiously and then frowned at her hesitation. 'What is the matter? He is only a horse like any other.'

'Hardly.' She glanced at the enormous animal warily before meeting Jay's eyes again. 'I'm only just getting used to Tabasco, and Firebrand suits me best of all.' He didn't respond to the humour and his frown deepened, slanting his piercing eyes into emerald slits.

'You are not frightened of these creatures?' His face darkened at her reluctant nod. '*Dios*! I thought that you would not accompany the boy and myself on our morning ride because you did not——' He stopped abruptly. 'This cannot be.' He slapped his hand hard against his muscled thigh. 'I will not have you worried by such gentle beasts.' Tornado rolled wicked eyes at her in the background as his master spoke, and snorted loudly, pawing the ground with his lethal hoofs.

Jay strode over to her and she took a hasty step backwards, looking down the stables to where Mateo was still laboriously grooming Tabasco. She needed a diversion, fast!

'I will teach you to ride,' he said commandingly.

She cast a horrified, desperate glance at Tornado and Jay's mouth twitched in a small smile.

'No, Jay, I don't want to, really. Horses don't like me.' She looked at him determinedly. 'They try and bite me.'

'Nonsense.' He shook his head slightly as he stood over her, his dark face implacable. 'I do not know what sort of animals you have been in contact with in the past, but none of my horses would dream of biting such a beautiful lady.' As he looked down at her, hard-muscled arms crossed and legs slightly apart, she could almost believe him. If he made his wishes known to the horses she was sure they wouldn't have the nerve to disobey

him, but she wasn't a horse and he might as well learn
that now.

'I will give you Toltec, Tabasco's sister. She is a gentle
and well-behaved young mare, and quite docile. You will
begin to ride every morning with Mateo and myself.' He
touched her flushed cheek as he spoke. 'And do not look
so concerned, little one. I promise I will keep you safe.'
There was something in his eyes that caused her heart
to thud and suddenly her fear of the horses was the least
of her worries.

'No. I've told you, I don't want to,' she said flatly as
she jerked away from his touch, her eyes flashing.

'It was not meant as a suggestion, Beth,' he said tightly
as anger flared coldly for a second in the green eyes.
'You will be ready at eight o'clock tomorrow.'

'I will not!' She forced herself to lower her voice as
Mateo looked up interestedly from the other end of the
stables. 'I'm employed to look after Mateo and that is
all. I don't have to learn to ride, for goodness' sake!'
She faced him angrily.

'I do not know about the sake of goodness but for
the sake of your spirit you will learn to ride.' His voice
was quite ruthless now and icy cold. 'I will not have
anyone who is in contact with my nephew behaving in
such a...' He was searching for the English word and
Beth finished the sentence for him.

'Cowardly way?' Two bright red spots of colour burnt
furiously in her cheeks and her grey eyes were black with
the force of her anger.

'The word I was going to use was "unwise" but if you
feel your choice is more appropriate...' His voice was
in perfect control and in stark contrast to Beth's shaking
hiss. 'You seem to forget you are in my employ, Miss
Kerri, and you will do exactly as you are told.' He shook
his head irritably as his rapier-sharp glance took in her

furious face, and said something that sounded extremely rude in his native tongue. 'Can you not see it is for your own benefit? The only way to deal with fear is to face it head-on and master it or it will master you in time.'

She almost stamped her foot in her frustration and rage. 'There's no need for me to face this particular... thing.' She would *not* give him the satisfaction of saying fear! 'Lots of people don't like horse-riding and——'

'Lots of people are not my responsibility. You are.'

'More's the pity.' She glared at him angrily. 'When I leave here I doubt if I'll ever see another horse except grazing in a field.'

His stance had stiffened at her words and now his voice was harsh as he bit out at her, 'When you leave here I do not care what you do.' He swung away and walked swiftly to the huge doors, his broad shoulders rigid and taut, pausing and fixing her face with his glacial stare before he left. 'But for now you are here on my ranch and you will do as I tell you. *Si*?'

She stared back defiantly. So much for giving him the benefit of the doubt. He was being utterly unreasonable—the man was a power-mad monster! 'You're the most——'

'I have the message, as you say.' There was a shutter over the dark face. 'Your face does your emotions credit. But you will be there. At eight. *Si*?' The voice was pure steel.

She shrugged coldly. 'I seem to have no choice.' He was like a cruel tyrant from his country's distant past and she loathed and detested him. How she loathed and detested him!

'That you do not,' he agreed silkily, his gaze glancing over her shoulder to where Mateo was standing looking towards them, brush in hand. 'I suggest you now go and reassure your charge that you are as obedient to me as you expect him to be to you.' He was adding insult to injury and he knew it!

She flounced round as he disappeared through the doors into the white sunlight beyond. Why had she let him get under her skin like that? She bit her bottom lip in an agony of frustration. She could have handled the whole situation far better, but her normal tact seemed to desert her when faced with his particular brand of cold arrogance. Now she was faced with something right out of her control and she was dreading it. Absolutely dreading it.

Later that night as she got ready for bed in the quietness of her room after a silent and very strained dinner with a grim Jay she felt a sharp lurch of panic at the thought of the proposed ride the next morning which intensified when she admitted to herself that it wasn't wholly her fear of the horses that was bothering her.

'How can you be so pathetic?' she said crossly to herself as she brushed her cap of blonde hair vigorously. Hadn't she learnt anything in the last twenty-five years? She looked at the pale-skinned, wide-eyed reflection in the mirror and grimaced angrily. 'He's just a man,' she told it through gritted teeth. 'Just a perfectly ordinary man.' The words didn't buoy her up as they had done in the past when she had applied them to her father after one of his ranting and raving exercises. Probably because in this case they were blatantly untrue.

She suddenly realised that her scalp was aching with her efforts, and threw down the brush bad-temperedly. Well, she'd just have to face it, wouldn't she, the way she had everything else unpleasant in her life? There was nowhere she could go. He had her trapped.

She awoke with a jerk long before dawn, her body wet with perspiration and her heart pounding. The dream. She had been dreaming—what was it? She lay quietly in the warm darkness as tiny snatches of the nightmare came back to her. She had been lost in a heat-laden silence on a vast, rocky, barren plain that was naked except for a few stunted trees. She had been running, she couldn't remember why, except that something had been chasing her, following her. She had taken refuge under one tree that stood out from all the others, being leafy and tall, and as she had sheltered under its protecting branches she had felt safe for a moment, until...

She sat up suddenly in the bed as she remembered. It had been there. The jaguar had been there. She had felt her eyes drawn upwards and as she had looked she had seen the big cat crouching indolently on a low branch just above her, its twitching tail a metronome of death. She couldn't remember what the body had looked like but she remembered the eyes—glittering, cruel green eyes that were lit with a cold fire. Eyes like——

'No!' She spoke aloud into the room. 'It was just a dream, only a dream!' She leapt out of bed, stripping off her damp nightie as she walked, and turning on the shower taps as her racing heartbeat slowly returned to normal. She stood under the warm water for long minutes, letting its clean caress relax her taut limbs and ease her mind. She was just apprehensive of the horse ride. Of course she was. There was nothing else to worry about. He hadn't even wanted her, after all. He had made that perfectly plain that night outside the stables after the walk. She must get control of herself, she must!

Jay was already in the dining-room when she followed the aroma of coffee an hour later, and he raised surprised eyes at her entrance. '*Buenos dias*, Beth.' He lowered his newspaper slowly. 'You are the very early bird.'

She smiled stiffly in reply but didn't speak, helping herself to a steaming cup of the hot liquid in silence.

'Would you care for something to eat?' he asked quietly as his eyes lingered on her pale face and the faint mauve shadows under her eyes.

'No, thank you.' She didn't look at him as she spoke and kept her voice bland and expressionless. If she had to do this she was blowed if she was going to be agreeable about it! He was so used to ordering everyone about——

'I agree. It is far better to enjoy the breakfast when one has been riding in the fresh morning air.' She heard him sigh softly as she kept her eyes on the rim of her cup. 'I was half expecting to have to come to your room and...persuade you out of bed.' She did look up, quickly, at that. There had been a note in his voice she didn't care to interpret.

'You should have known there would be no need for that,' she said sharply, and he smiled as he saw the enraged sparkle in her eyes.

'*Sí*. You are quite right. And now the adrenalin is pumping a little more robustly?'

She glared at him in reply. She might have known he had just been trying to get a reaction. He was the most irritating man.

'Come.' He moved swiftly as she finished her coffee, taking her arm in a firm grip and drawing her out of the room and across the huge hall before she could resist. 'Mateo will be along shortly but first I want you to meet Toltec and get familiar with her before you mount.'

'It's not eight yet,' she protested faintly as the warm morning air kissed her face with the sweet perfume of a hundred flowers in its lazy depths as he closed the front door behind them. The sky was glimmering a bright steel-blue, polished and sharp in the morning sun, and as they neared the stable block the fresh smell of clean straw replaced the perfume in the air.

She was always amazed at the pristine cleanliness of the building that housed the horses, but as she glanced sideways at the big, silent figure towering over her she supposed she shouldn't be. Jay expected, and received, the very best care of his valuable stock, and it hadn't taken her long to recognise that as well as being his main business interest the horses were his life. They were in his blood, just like his young nephew, and as far as he was concerned the ranch hands were extremely fortunate to even come into contact with such beautiful animals. She slanted another quick glance under her lashes. He had probably taken it as a personal insult that she was afraid of his darlings.

On reaching the huge wooden doors he pushed one open and drew her into the quiet sunlit building. 'Come and say hello to your friend.' He led her to Toltec's stall and she put out a tentative hand to the dark brown velvet muzzle thrust out towards her. She had to admit that this gentle, docile animal bore no resemblance to the fiery mass of razor-sharp teeth and hoofs that made up Tornado.

'Stand right by her, *pequeña*. She is as gentle as a new-born lamb, aren't you, my pretty?' He was close, too close, and as she hesitated he took a step forward and brought her round firmly in front of him so that his arms were imprisoning her on either side and the horse was in front of her.

'Just relax, little one. She wants to like you; make it easy for her.' His voice was a soft murmur in her ear and she could feel his clean breath lift the silk of her hair as he spoke, his big body a hard wall behind her.

She forced herself to reach out and touch the velvet nose and was rewarded by a swift feeling of elation as Toltec pushed gently into her hand.

'Now just touch and feel her. Get used to her. Treat her as kindly as you would a lover.' She knew he was being deliberately provocative, but, sandwiched as she was between the horse and his body, she strove to ignore the increasing warmth in her cheeks. This was typical arrogant male strategy!

She stroked the shining flank of the animal almost automatically, every inch of her vitally aware of that steel-hard frame against hers. 'There. That is not so bad, is it?' He had bent to whisper in her ear again and she couldn't hide the shudder that ran through her at the feel of his firm mouth against her flesh. She had the notion that he hadn't been talking merely about the horse, an impression that was confirmed when he turned her gently to face him, his arms holding her captive and at the same time protecting.

'Beth?' His quiet voice was asking a question that she was incapable of answering, and as she stared up into his dark, searingly handsome face she knew he was going to kiss her and wanted it more than she had ever wanted anything in her life. 'Oh, Beth...' His voice was a soft groan and as he lowered his head to take her lips, pulling her closer into his body, she started violently as a high childish voice called out gaily from just outside the open doors,

'Gran Jay! Beth! Are you in there?'

Jay swore softly and vehemently as she moved quickly out of his embrace, her cheeks scarlet, and the next moment Mateo burst through the opening, his big brown eyes bright and his face merry.

'Are you coming with us, Beth? Really?' He was clearly delighted at the prospect, and she saw Jay's eyes soften as the small boy ran to her outstretched arms, lifting his face expectantly for her morning kiss.

'Of course Beth is coming with us. I told you she hopes to ride as well as you do one day. You are early today, are you not?' Jay was smiling indulgently now and he ruffled the boy's black curls as he passed by to get the saddles for the horses.

That first morning ride was a very sedate affair but even so by evening Beth felt as though every muscle in her legs and lower torso was screaming protest. She had been so intent on staying put on Toltec's broad back that the ride had been over before she relaxed, but even so the feel of the animal's warm body beneath hers and the sparkling light and pure air had left a pleasant memory all day.

Jay and Mateo had been very patient, the latter somewhat condescendingly so, but she sensed that the novelty of her presence had worn thin for her small charge by the end of the ride. He had clearly been longing for his usual gallop with his uncle over the sun-washed plain below a sky swept clean of even one tiny cloud, and Beth had noticed the occasional warning glance Jay had flashed at his nephew when the small boy's high spirits had threatened to break loose.

After a week of tolerant patience by Jay and resigned long-suffering by Mateo, she had reached the stage where a controlled trot was not beyond her, and would often stop halfway on the ride, encouraging the two males to take off on a wild, unrestrained gallop across the short tufted grass while she sat idly on Toltec's solid back and watched them.

It always did crazy things to her equilibrium to see Jay at this stage of the ride. He seemed at one with the huge powerful black stallion he controlled so easily and as he thundered across the plain with Mateo in hot pursuit he looked for all the world as though he had stepped back in time, a dangerous, cruel *conquistador* intent on rape and pillage and total domination. She didn't try and analyse her feelings with regard to the proud ruler of this tiny kingdom any more—they were too complicated and it was too unsettling. She merely made sure that she was never alone with him except at the dinner table, when she made a point of leaving quickly after coffee, maintained a distant, cool exterior when he was around, and prayed avidly every night that he would leave her alone. He seemed to accept the situation and yet she had the uncomfortable feeling now and again that he was merely biding his time, lulling her into a false sense of security.

This feeling was very strong the evening Mateo left to visit Felicia's mother for the weekend in Guadalajara. The small boy had asked her to go with him several times, but Jay had firmly squashed the notion, insisting that the invitation was just for Mateo. 'But Aunt Sofía won't mind, Gran Jay,' Mateo had protested tearfully. 'I want Beth with me. I want to show her the birds and everything.'

'You will not both fit into her tiny house now that Felicia is home,' Jay chided softly as he settled Mateo into the helicopter beside Luis. 'Be brave, *niño*, you will be seeing your Beth again soon.'

She had noticed that since the night of the foaling gentleness was uppermost in his dealing with the child, but not at the cost of discipline. Mateo rarely got his own way unless Jay was feeling particularly indulgent.

He would make a wonderful father. The thought jumped unbidden into her mind as they waved Mateo off until the helicopter was a tiny silver speck against great, still clouds edged with the glittering golden rays of the dying sun. It caused her mouth to open in a silent gasp of shock and her heart to pound as she swiftly denied the idea. Of course he wouldn't. He'd make a terrible father, just like hers in fact—cold, overbearing and with no compassion or tenderness. Even as she tried to persuade herself it was true, her innate honesty forced her to admit that she was having to put up quite an argument.

'I do not normally have to persuade him to visit Felicia's mother,' Jay said wryly, and she glanced up to find the glittering green gaze tight on her face. 'He has always enjoyed his time there. The family are very old friends, and since Sofía's husband died five years ago she looks forward to seeing Mateo on a regular basis. Felicia is often away. She has a wide circle of friends.'

She nodded dismissively. 'If you'll excuse me...'

'As you say. Dinner at eight, then.' He strode ahead of her, the two massive guard-dogs bounding at his heels as he made a detour towards the stables. She followed slowly, making for the hacienda, feeling unaccountably depressed. It was just because Mateo would be away for the weekend—she would miss his cheerful chatter, she told herself resolutely. Still, a weekend alone would give her time to catch up on her reading and maybe she could even do a little painting. She had brought her brushes and a few tubes of paint with her and the hacienda had been begging to be captured on canvas for weeks, the blaze of vibrant bougainvillaea and hibiscus against mellow stone a wonderful contrast to the sun-slashed shade of the fruit trees.

Just before dinner as she was preparing to get ready Rosa's timid knock sounded at the door. The little maid informed her, with many gestures and much arm-waving, that the *señor* had been called out unexpectedly on business, and would she care for a tray in her room? The feeling of depression grew and was still with Beth later that night as she slipped under the cool covers and settled down for sleep. Still, at least she would be spared the morning ride tomorrow, with Mateo away. The depression became a thick grey cloud that sat over her head with obstinate determination, and at last, thoroughly irritated with herself for no good reason, she pulled the pillow over her head and sought oblivion in sleep.

The first realisation that it was morning, and that the tossing and turning of the long night was finished, was a cool, hard hand on her shoulder. Her eyes snapped wide open at the same time as she started violently. Eight years of waking alone had not conditioned her to such an abrupt start to the day.

'I am sorry. I startled you?' As her grey eyes fastened on the cold steel in Jay's she saw that he didn't look at all sorry. In fact he looked angry. Very angry.

'Is anything the matter?' She half rose in the bed and then sank back down under the covers in an anxious flush as she realised that the thin silk of her nightie was almost transparent. 'Did you knock?' she asked crossly.

'Did I knock?' He repeated her words with a slightly incredulous scowl darkening his face. 'No, I did not knock. I have been waiting for...' he glanced at the heavy gold watch on his brown wrist '...exactly twenty minutes. I think it is for me to ask if anything is the matter.'

'Waiting?' For a moment she couldn't bring herself round sufficiently to think, and then as hot colour flooded into her cheeks she realised that he had expected her at the stables.

'But I thought...with Mateo away...we wouldn't——'

'Mateo is a consideration to your accompanying me in the morning?' Now she saw that she had really made him angry as dull red seared the high cheekbones and turned the green eyes glacial. 'Why?'

The one word was stark and uncompromising and she didn't know how to reply. She could hardly say that she didn't want to be alone with him. She should have said something yesterday, made herself clear, but he had been busy in the day and then had disappeared for the evening. She looked at him helplessly. 'Well, it's just that...'

'Just that?' He repeated her words in icy mockery and suddenly her temper rose to match his. How dared he barge into her room like this? Surely she was entitled to a little privacy?

'I don't think this is the time or place to discuss it,' she said coldly, and his eyes narrowed, a cruel rawness turning them almost black as he glared down at her, arms crossed.

'Discuss it? Discuss what?' he said bitingly. 'The fact that there might be just a little crack in the oh, so big fence that you have carefully built around yourself? The fence from behind which you peep out at the cruel oppressor who torments you?'

'I don't know what you are talking about,' she said furiously.

'No? Then why are you so frightened to ride alone with me? Do you really think I am going to drag you from your horse and lay you out on the ground and rape you? Is that what you think, my little English mouse?'

'I am not a mouse.' She raised her head proudly as her eyes flashed grey sparks. 'I just didn't think you'd want to ride this morning, that's all.' She pulled the sheet round her as she sat up, her blonde hair tousled and her body stiff. She felt at an acute disadvantage lying in bed semi-naked while he was fully dressed, which added to her resentment. 'And there was no need to barge into my room, either.'

'Barge? What is this barge? If you mean I should have stood outside and meekly requested permission to enter then that is your second mistake this morning. Now you will get out of bed and get dressed and be at the stables in five minutes. Do you understand me?' His voice was soft now and even, but the glittering of his eyes and the harsh lines of his dark face told her that he intended to be obeyed.

She didn't know what little demon made her push him still further, and even as she spoke her next words she knew that she was being incredibly foolish. 'And if I refuse?' Grey eyes clashed with green and she forced herself not to lower her eyes beneath the power of his gaze.

'But you will not refuse, will you, little one?' It was a statement, not a question. 'You would like to believe that I repel you, that you feel the revulsion for me, is that not so?' He bent down over her as he spoke until his face was on a level with hers, putting his hands either side of the bed so that she was forced to slide down under the covers or meet his face. 'But we both know that, whatever your head feels, your body is more discerning. If I decided to make love to you out there on the plain or anywhere else it would not be rape, my little silver-haired siren. And if you do not wish me to do that very thing, now, here in your own bed, you will do as I command and join me for the pleasant morning ride. *Sì*?'

She felt such a tide of hate and rage consume her that for a moment his body misted in her vision. How dared he? He was forcing her to recognise his domination over her and the most bitterly galling thing of all was that she dared not call his bluff. If he touched her she didn't trust herself not to succumb, and a flush of humiliation made her want to weep.

'I am waiting, Beth. You join me on the ride?' His voice was silky smooth and perfectly in control. He knew he had won.

'Yes.' It was a tiny whisper but filled with such enmity that if she had been looking at him she would have seen a flash of pain shadow his eyes for the briefest of moments.

'Good. Five minutes, then, and do not keep me waiting.'

She was ready in less, stalking across to the stables where he was waiting astride Tornado while a young ranch hand held Toltec's reins in his hand. 'Thanks, Pedro.' She flashed the youth a quick smile as he helped her up and then turned a stony face to Jay. 'Well? Shall we get started?'

His face went a shade harder at her audacity in addressing him in such an abrupt manner in front of one of his employees, but he merely inclined his head slowly, while the look in his eyes made her flush scarlet. She hated this man. She really hated him.

'*Gracias*, Pedro.' As the young man opened the heavy gates that led out into the plain, away from the stables and the racetrack, Jay thanked him and then cantered through with Beth following behind, and for a moment it seemed symbolic of everything that had happened to her since she had met this autocratic, cruel tyrant. He led and she followed like the little mouse he had accused her of being.

Well, no more! As she followed him out on to the grass-tufted wilderness overlooked by quiet, sunburnt hills, she made a promise to herself that she was determined to keep. When she left this place she would take enormous pleasure in telling this megalomaniac exactly what she thought of him! In the last few weeks she had realised that she couldn't leave Mateo until they both went to England—the child had captured her heart with his small hands and she couldn't bear the thought of leaving him to think that she hadn't really cared. Her life was bound up with him for the next few months, and once in England she could get a post near his school and visit him regularly, but effectively she would be free of his uncle. Wouldn't she? She ignored the question mark in her mind with ruthless determination, her eyes inward-looking and her face set as she swayed in easy rhythm on the mare's big, warm back.

CHAPTER SIX

THE ride was conducted in total silence, and once back at the ranch after breakfast Beth disappeared to her room for the rest of the morning, more shaken than she cared to admit by the battle of wills. The afternoon dragged without Mateo's happy presence and she found herself missing her small charge intensely. By evening a very definite headache had settled itself behind her eyes.

She would have liked to ask for a tray in her room for dinner but hadn't the strength to endure another confrontation, so promptly at eight she appeared in the dining-room, outwardly calm and inwardly on fire, to find Jay sitting in relaxed conversation with two young American men who had come to view the horses. Their presence made the meal bearable and when they left to catch their night flight she made quickly for her room, congratulating herself on escaping so easily from that rapier-sharp gaze that had sliced into her more than once during the course of the evening.

She had barely closed the door when a light but authoritative knock sounded outside, causing her heart to dive into her shoes. 'Come in.' She knew who it was even before Jay's dark, mocking face peered round the door.

'You see—I knocked?' The voice was lazy and faintly amused and in view of her own feelings of turmoil an added insult. He walked indolently across the room to where she was sitting at the large ornate dressing-table preparatory to removing her light make-up, and she glanced up at him warily.

'Yes? Do you want something?' His eyes glanced wickedly to the bed for an instant and as she coloured a vivid pink he turned away, but not before she had seen a small smile tug at the firm lips at her reaction.

Mouse be blowed! As a mixture of hurt and rage flooded her chest she stiffened tightly. 'I said do you want something? If not I'd like to get ready for bed, please, so if you don't mind...' She waved her hand to the door but the effort it took to control her voice was wasted as the burning colour washing her face betrayed her rage.

'Yes, I want something.' His voice was bland now and his face quite devoid of expression as he turned to face her again halfway across the room. 'I would like to take you to see Lake Chapala tomorrow—the largest lake in Mexico, you understand? If you could be ready by nine we will leave directly after breakfast.'

For a second she thought she had misheard him and then as her mouth opened in a small 'O' of amazement the surprise was replaced by anger. After this morning? The man was mad! 'I'm sorry. I've made plans for tomorrow.'

'Cancel them.' His voice was soft but definite, and as she opened her mouth to argue further he crossed the room again in two strides and knelt down before her so that his head was on a level with her and his eyes were looking straight into hers. She was aware of the powerful breadth of him and the way his trousers pulled taut over his thighs in the split-second before he took one of her hands where it rested on her lap and placed it briefly to his lips. '*Por favor*?'

There was something in the warmth of his glance that made her as weak as a kitten, and he was still holding her hand. The brilliant green of his eyes, the tanned skin relieved momentarily by the thin silver scar, the jet-black straight hair against the snowy whiteness of his shirt all had her mesmerised, and she felt a sudden rush of longing—but for what she didn't know.

'All right.' She heard herself speak the words with something akin to horror and her eyes must have revealed something of what she was feeling because he touched her soft cheek lightly as he stood up, his eyes hooded.

'Poor baby.' She looked up sharply, expecting mockery or derision, but she couldn't have described the look on his face that suddenly made her tremble and achingly hot. 'So mixed up and so lovely.' He lifted a strand of shining blonde hair and let it trail through his fingers to rest against her pink cheek. 'Till tomorrow, little one, and I promise you I shall behave, as you say, like the gentleman.'

As the door closed behind him she realised she was shaking and hoped he hadn't noticed, but, of course, he would have. Nothing missed that piercing gaze. She twisted on the embroidered stool in an agony of confusion. Had she really promised to spend the day with him? And she had thought *him* mad! What on earth had possessed her?

What did he want with her? She remembered the look on that dark face and her stomach twisted. She *knew* what he wanted, and yet... The night after the foaling burnt vividly in her mind and her mouth hardened in anger and humiliation. He could have taken her then and he knew it. She didn't understand any of this, and least of all herself. He was playing with her, like a cat with a mouse. She got ready for bed almost mechanically and as she slipped under the cool covers she expected to lie awake for hours, but was asleep within minutes, to dream soundlessly until morning.

*   *   *

'What do you think of this oh, so famous lake?' They were sitting quietly on a secluded slope on the southern shore of the lake, and in the distance at the northern edge a line of villages glittered tantalisingly in the afternoon sun, and just to the left of them, to add to the sense of unreality, bright blue flowers were entwined over a mass of trees and bushes, creating a spider-web tracery of indigo, sapphire and jade-green.

'It's a beautiful spot.' She glanced at Jay lying stretched out on the woven blanket at her side, his fingers sticky with the juice of the fresh peaches Juana had added to their lunch basket, and wished she could feel as relaxed as he was. He had taken off his shirt, much to her consternation, after gravely asking her permission, which she could hardly refuse, and his powerful bronzed chest lay exposed to the sun, the mass of dark hair a vivid contrast to the gaily embroidered rug. How could you have come here? she berated herself angrily.

Far in the distance wrinkled old men, gnarled and bent with age, tended their voracious goats on the grassy slopes, their thickly woven serapes tight around their thin bodies in spite of the heat of the day; but here all was solitude and quietness, except for the mad beating of her heart.

'Why do you not lie back and enjoy the sun?' Jay's gaze slanted at her as she sat, stiff and upright, by his side. 'It is not so hot to burn the English skin and already you are a more ... acceptable shade of brown.'

'Acceptable?' She snapped her gaze down at the overt criticism to see a teasing smile touching the hard mouth. 'Huh!'

'But that hair.' He reached up a long hand and took a handful in his fingers, drawing her backwards on to the ground. 'There is nothing we can do to disguise such paleness. No true Spaniard ever had such a colour of hair.' She was lying by his side now, his hand still entwined in the silkiness of her hair, and he raised himself up on one elbow to look down at her, his skin gleaming in the light with a coppery tinge.

'I don't want to disguise it,' she said immediately as she looked up into his dark face, her eyes sparking angrily.

'No?' His voice was thick and unsteady and his eyes were burning, and just for a moment she was breathlessly afraid of the tautness in his body and the harsh desire in his face, but then he bent his head to take her lips in a demanding, hungry kiss and she ceased to think, her whole body alive with a fierce, raging thirst. She reached up to him, wrapping her slim arms round his neck, and as he felt her softness against him he groaned deep in his throat, his hands moving over her body in feverish exploration. No! It mustn't happen again.

His lips trailed fire over her eyes, her ears, her throat, returning to her open mouth with a renewed hunger that had her trembling against him in an agony of need. His hands were gentle as they guided her body along and she heard the little cries being torn from her lips with a feeling of wonderment. She had never known it could be like this, that her whole being could be so totally alive—but it must stop, now!

'Beth... So sweet, so innocent... I must have you.'

As his murmurings reached that tiny untouched place in her mind she felt a sudden sense of panic that quenched the madness that had taken hold of her like cold water, and reacted violently, pushing at him with hands that were strong in her fright.

'No! Leave me.' As she twisted away he made no effort to hold her, sitting up in one movement and holding his head in his hands as his laboured breathing slowly returned to normal, and the natural sounds of the birds and droning insects made themselves heard again above the clamouring of her heart.

'It is all right, Beth. I would not have hurt you.' His voice was quiet as he raised his head to look into her burning face, but she couldn't disguise the trembling that seemed to have taken possession of her limbs.

'Who is it, Beth? Who has hurt you so badly?' His green eyes were reflecting the clear brilliance of the sky, and seemed almost turquoise as he stared hard at her. 'When I hold you in my arms I sense that this is all new to you. That you have never had a man love you in this way. And yet someone has hurt you, have they not?'

'Don't; I don't want to talk about it. Just leave me alone.' She leapt up in her agitation and walked up the gently undulating slope on legs that were shaking, standing with her arms hugged tightly round her as she looked out over the lake that shimmered and sparkled in the heat-blasting light. She couldn't, dared not trust him, couldn't come under his control until she was just a thing with no mind of her own. This was madness, crazy. She mustn't succumb to it. He had had countless women; this meant nothing to him.

He was packing the picnic basket when she wandered back, and after one swift, searching glance at her strained face he continued in his task without speaking, his face closed and sombre and his movements calm and precise.

The long ride home was through stretches of empty countryside that gave way to villages with narrow cobbled streets, quiet and shadowed in the evening sun, with white-walled, red-tiled houses enclosed by hedges of pink and lavender hibiscus and flowering vines spread over roofs and fences alive with orange and purple blooms. The atmosphere in the car was alive with tension so fierce that Beth felt she could taste it. Outside the birds were calling and singing with unrestrained enthusiasm but inside all was silent and heavy.

Dusk had come and gone by the time they reached the ranch, and the night sky was a soft indigo brilliant with a million shining, blinking stars. She was out of the car almost before Jay cut the engine, preceding him into the hacienda quickly and keeping her head bent so that the smooth flush of her hair hid most of her face from his troubled gaze.

'I'd like to go straight to bed if that's all right?' She faced him for a brief moment in the deserted hall and he nodded slowly.

'Of course, Beth. You are free to do as you wish while under my protection.' She had the funniest notion he was trying to tell her something more than the mere words conveyed but immediately dismissed it as fanciful. Much more of this and they would be taking her back to England in a strait-jacket! She didn't recognise herself any more. Back to England? She ignored the sickening lurch her heart gave and nodded brightly at him with a false, brittle smile.

'Goodnight, then, and thank you for a lovely day.'

'The pleasure was all mine, Beth. I deeply enjoyed your company.' His voice and face were devoid of all mockery or censure and she suddenly knew that if she didn't reach the sanctuary of her room soon she would disgrace herself still further by bursting into a torrent of weeping. She had never felt so totally miserable in all her life, or so hopelessly confused.

Sleep eluded her for hours and when she finally slept, hot, weary and heartsore, it was to dream the dream of *el tigre* again and wake, panic-stricken and panting, as dawn touched its soft pink fingers to the budding sky.

It was early afternoon before she saw Jay again, and her stomach had been turning over all day. The memory of their intimate embraces was burnt on her consciousness and she fluctuated between hot embarrassment, deep humiliation and cold anger at both him and herself until her head was throbbing like a drum. He had been out at his late brother's ranch all morning, attending to some business there, and she ate lunch alone in her room, curled up with a book in which she had no interest at all. Mateo was due back that evening and time hung heavy.

The afternoon was hot and still and the very air seemed to shimmer with the sharpness of a diamond, which increased the pounding in her head, so after a while she opened the shutters in her room and strolled out into the ornately tiled, shade-filled courtyard. The decorative palms with their enormous, graceful fronds and lemon and lime trees provided a tranquil escape from the burning sun, and a profusion of flowering bushes and shrubs sprinkled with luminous blooms of yellow, red and orange perfumed the air with a delicate fragrance that attracted huge, brightly coloured butterflies and tiny birds.

Beth sat down on one of the wooden seats close to the fountain from which water fell continuously in a transparent silver sheath and shut her eyes, letting the peace and quiet calm her mind and wash away the ache of uncertainty about her future. She wasn't aware that she had fallen into a light doze but as she felt something brush across her lips she opened her eyes sleepily to find Jay's dark face inches away from hers.

'Hello.' His jet-black hair was illuminated by a slender shaft of sunlight through the greenery, and as she went to move he quickly sat down beside her, restraining her with a light touch on her arm. 'Sit still, Beth. There is no need to fly from me like a doe before the hunter.'

'I was just resting for a moment.' She smoothed her hair irritably, annoyed at the innuendo and searching for a scathing rebuff, starting visibly as his hand went out to touch the faint mauve shadows under her eyes.

'You did not sleep well?' There was a wealth of tenderness in his voice and for a moment, just for a moment, she was tempted to believe it was genuine. Then cold reason swamped the desire and she moved abruptly, shrugging her shoulders in careless nonchalance.

'No, not really. It wasn't as cool as usual last night, was it?' The excuse was weak but all she could manage.

'I do not tend to notice such things, having lived here all my life.' He paused for a fraction of a second as though considering if he should speak his next words. 'I, nevertheless, did not rest much either.'

She glanced up sharply at that and met his tight green gaze fixed on her face. 'You didn't?' Her voice was carefully cool and then his lips touched her smooth brow in a light kiss. She forced herself to remain motionless.

'No, I did not, and that is unusual for me.' He sighed softly at her stiff, closed face and then drew her into his side, resting her head against the pure white linen covering his chest and quietly stroking the smooth silk of her hair as he talked. 'I do not know what it is that troubles you so completely, little one, but you have nothing to fear from me. I would like you to believe that.' She kept perfectly still.

'I see.' Her voice was loaded with scorn. 'And yesterday?'

'Yesterday was a mistake.' His voice was still quiet but with a touch of regret in its depths. 'I went too fast for you and I am sorry, but...' his green eyes held that touch of fire again '...I am a man and you are very beautiful.'

She could feel the pink stealing into her cheeks and tried to move away, but he was holding her fast. 'I don't think——'

'No, no. Do not think. I am beginning to feel that you *think* far too much. One minute so soft and yielding like temptation itself and the next a small, spitting bundle of fur, but always, always beautiful.' She sat, mesmerised, as his deep, rich voice and glittering eyes made love to her, feeling almost as though he was caressing her body as his dark gaze wandered over her face and hair. 'There is so much you have to learn, little one, and we can go as slow as you like.' He bent forward and captured her lips as he spoke in a slow, melting kiss that had her trembling against his hard chest in moments. The clean, fresh smell of him filled her nostrils and she longed to reach up and touch his face, his hair, but the memory of yesterday was too strong and so she remained quivering and stiff in his hold until he raised his head again to look down into her upturned face.

'Will you trust me, just a little, my sweet one?' He cupped her chin in the palm of his hand as he spoke, looking deep into her soft grey eyes, his expression freezing as his name was called, gently and huskily, from the open doorway into his study.

As they turned, still in an embrace, to see Felicia's tall, slender form silhouetted against the darkness of the room, Mateo burst past her with a delighted squeal to fling himself wholesale into Beth's arms, his small face alight with joy. 'Have you missed me? Have you, Beth?'

'Terribly,' she assured him lovingly as she hugged him to her, kissing the small face lifted up to her. Jay had risen immediately and walked to Felicia's side, drawing her into the courtyard with his arm round her tiny waist. 'I think you have met Beth, have you not?' He looked down into Felicia's huge liquid eyes and the young woman nodded slowly before turning to Beth with a tight smile on her beautiful face.

'*Buenas tardes*, Beth. I glad you are the—how you say?—servant for Mateo.'

'Governess, Felicia,' Jay corrected with a small frown. 'Your English has not improved, I see.' Felicia laughed up into his dark face with a provocative pout to her full red lips but Beth had the feeling that the word had been chosen deliberately as a means of putting her in her place. There had been a hardness in those dark brown eyes like splintered flint in the first few seconds she had beheld Felicia's face before Mateo had arrived on the scene, and now the woman was glued to Jay's side like a second skin.

'You have come to stay?' Jay seemed oblivious to any tension, or maybe he just didn't care? Beth thought angrily. She was only the 'governess' after all! She had nearly forgotten.

'If you want me?' Felicia gave the cute little giggle that Beth remembered from their brief meeting in England, and Jay smiled indulgently into the lovely olive-skinned face looking up at him so adoringly before kissing her gently.

'Of course we want you. Is that not right, Mateo?' Mateo clearly didn't care much one way or the other but at his uncle's frown he gave a moderately enthusiastic reply before taking Beth's hand and drawing her to her feet.

'Come and see the songbird that Aunt Sofía has given me. She has hundreds! Felicia has bought me a big bamboo cage so I may keep it—may I not, Gran Jay?' The request was clearly an afterthought and he looked anxiously into Jay's face. 'It was the biggest cage at the market so she has lots of room.'

'In that case I think we had better get a mate for her the next time we are in Guadalajara,' Jay said thoughtfully. 'It is not good for a female to be alone too long.' His emerald-green eyes swept Beth's face for a brief moment, causing her to stiffen and flush hotly at the innuendo he meant just for her ears, but as she turned from his glance, her eyes angry, she saw that Felicia's mouth had pulled into a thin line. She suddenly had the feeling that Felicia would miss nothing, however small, where Jay was concerned.

'I sorry I not come before.' Now the beautiful face was all sweetness as she looked up into Jay's face. 'I go South of France. With Roberto. But he get too...serious. I no like.' She pouted, obviously waiting for a reaction, her eyes eating him.

'Another broken heart?' Jay said gallantly. 'The world must be strewn with them.' He brushed her cheek with a teasing finger.

'Oh, you!' She pushed against him in possessive intimacy and Beth was glad of Mateo's chatter and his small body pressed close to her. She suddenly felt very cold and alone and incredibly angry. Whatever the relationship was between Felicia and Jay, it was clearly more than just 'friends'. How dared he talk to her as he had done, just a few minutes ago, when all the time——?

'You show me horses now?' Felicia moved slightly as she spoke so that her back was towards Beth and she was between her and Jay, effectively cutting the two of them off in their own little world. 'Si?' She wound her slim arms round Jay's neck, standing on tiptoe.

'Of course.' Jay stepped to one side and ruffled his nephew's hair as he spoke. 'Is there anyone here who wants to see Firebrand?'

'Me! Me!' Mateo took his uncle's hand as he spoke with his other still gripping Beth's tightly, and so they left the courtyard, the irony of the situation bringing a wry smile to Beth's lips for a fleeting moment. Felicia's face was a picture in outraged pride.

The rest of the afternoon and evening was taut with a tenseness that Beth felt Jay must sense. She had made a hesitant overture of friendship at the stables which had been well and truly snubbed by Felicia after the Mexican girl had checked that Jay was out of earshot, and dinner had been an uncomfortable affair for Beth with Felicia recalling past events, ensuring that the conversation was one in which Beth could play no part. She was glad to make the excuse of a headache and escape early to her room, noticing the satisfied sneer on Felicia's face with mixed feelings. Jay had looked surprised but not unduly perturbed at her swift exit and by the time she had showered and climbed into bed the incident in the courtyard was fast fading into a forgotten dream. Thank goodness Felicia had arrived when she did! She, Beth, might have been fooled into believing Jay's empty words—the Mexican girl's arrival was the best thing that could have happened.

She recalled the softness in his harsh face when he had looked at Felicia, their easy embraces, and felt such a stab of pain in her heart region that she gasped out loud. 'What's the matter with me?' she whispered into the velvet darkness as she searched for sleep. 'I want him to leave me alone, don't I? That's what I want.' She twisted angrily in the bed, despising herself for her confusion and Jay for his shallowness.

She had just finished dressing the next morning and was brushing her hair into a silky bob when a light knock sounded at her door. 'Come in.' She looked up apprehensively.

As Felicia sauntered into the room Beth noticed with a sinking of her heart that the Mexican girl looked even more breathtakingly lovely in the clear morning light. She was dressed with seeming casualness in a scarlet sundress that clung to her slender body like a second skin before flaring out in a wide, full skirt that brought attention to her slim, shapely legs and tiny ankles. Her glossy black hair was loose and hung almost to her waist, and her large dark brown eyes with their fringe of rich thick lashes were set like jewels in her clear, almost transparent skin. She looked warm and voluptuous and sensual, a vision to stir any man's blood.

'*Buenos dias*. Oh, I sorry. Good morning.' She gave a smile that didn't reach the ebony stone of her eyes.

'It's all right, I do know a little Spanish now.' Beth smiled pleasantly, refusing to acknowledge the scornful barb in the softly drawled words.

'You do? *Bravo*!' Felicia gave a soundless contemptuous clap of her hands before turning and shutting the door carefully. 'How long that you stay here?' Her tone and face made no effort to make the question anything but a challenge.

'Until Mateo goes to England,' Beth said shortly as she let her eyes hold Felicia's hard gaze. If that was the way Felicia wanted to play it, fine. She needed her friendship like a hole in the head.

'I see.' The Mexican girl wandered across to the dressing-table and idly moved a bottle of perfume across the polished surface with a red talon of a fingernail. 'You like it here?'

'I always enjoy my work with children.' Beth turned back to the mirror and continued brushing her hair, watching Felicia's face in its reflection. 'And Mateo is a lovely child.'

'You like to be . . . governess?' The incredulous note in the husky voice was clearly meant as an insult. 'I find that very strange.'

'Do you?' Beth counted to ten and kept her voice calm. 'Don't you like children?'

Felicia shrugged gracefully like a satisfied, sleek cat. 'They bore me.' She crossed the room and picked up one of the magazines Jay had bought Beth on her first day, flicking through the pages indolently before slinging it down so that it slid on the floor along with several others. She made no effort to retrieve them.

'Did you want something?' Beth's temper had flared to ignition level at the other girl's cool, calculated insolence, and she held on to her control by sheer willpower, blessing the years of training with difficult children that enabled her to master her irritation. Funny that it worked with everyone but Jay—but then, he was in a class of his own for arrogance.

As though the thought of his name had transferred itself to Felicia she turned sharply and walked to the door, pausing meaningfully before opening it. 'Jay is mine, *si*? You do not have him.' Beth stared at her, rendered speechless by the sudden openness of the attack. 'If you try I stop you.'

'Now look here——'

'No. I no look anywhere.' Felicia had opened the door and disappeared before Beth could say any more, leaving only the musky, heavy scent of her perfume in the air to convince Beth that the little drama had actually happened.

The day didn't improve as it went on. At breakfast Felicia dominated the conversation, her every word and gesture making it crystal-clear that there was no one in the room for her but the tall, dark man opposite. When she began to feed him a cluster of grapes from the fruit bowl, one by one, Beth felt physically sick.

'Your headache is better?' Jay had seemed a little cool when she had joined them at the table, and now, on her glance of enquiry, Felicia spoke quickly, her voice soft and warm but her eyes as deadly as a cobra's.

'I tell Jay you no come with us early. You have the headache. Is best sleep——' She smiled sweetly.

'Just do not make it a habit, Beth.' Jay's voice cut in on Felicia's with a hard warning in its smooth depths, and then Felicia changed the conversation before Beth could make the protest hovering on her lips. Mateo had slept late and so she had assumed the morning ride was off, but apparently Felicia had engineered Jay all to herself, while making the sort of excuse that was guaranteed to put Beth in a bad light.

The Mexican girl was certainly serious about Jay being hers, it appeared! Beth fought her rising anger. They must be lovers... How long had they shared such intimacy? She ignored the twisting lurch her heart gave and concentrated on her toast and preserve, willing her heart to resume its normal steady beat instead of running away like an express train.

'You take me see Alfredo's home today?' Felicia wheedled as they finished breakfast, touching Jay's hard-muscled arm imploringly.

'What do you want to go there for?' Mateo asked with a childish lack of tact. 'There is nothing to see there; all the fun is here with the horses and——'

'I go see. Remember Alfredo.' Felicia cast a glance that would have floored Mateo if he had been looking at her, but as it was it was a totally wasted use of energy as the small boy was concentrating with whole-hearted devotion on the mound of toast he was demolishing.

'Do you really want to go?' Jay asked with a note of surprise in his voice.

'*Sí*. To remember.' Felicia smiled a careful, sad smile.

'Funny child.' His face held the usual indulgent warmth that was normally present when he looked at her. 'Well, we can go across in the Range Rover if you like. You will come, Mateo, Beth?' The dark green gaze on her was challenging.

For a moment Beth was tempted to agree just to wipe the cat-with-the-cream expression off Felicia's lovely face, but she was experiencing such burning rage at the continuous, nauseating, tête-à-tête that she knew she couldn't control herself for a whole day.

'Mateo?' She knew what the decision would be if left to her small charge. The child never wanted to visit his old home and she suspected that besides his great love for the horses and the hacienda there were too many bad memories buried deep in his subconscious to make any trip there anything but an ordeal. Jay insisted his small nephew accompany him back now and again, trying to engender some pride in his inheritance, but Beth was of the conviction that for once he was losing a battle.

'Can we stay here, Beth?' Mateo looked up at her, his large eyes spaniel-like. 'I've been away for three days and I want to see Firebrand today.' She heaved a silent sigh of relief.

'I don't see why not.' She smiled at him, ignoring the others.

'It is you and I, Jay.' Felicia reached across and touched the hard, tanned cheek with the scar in an intimate, loving gesture. 'We ride, *sí*? I go change. No car.'

'If it pleases you.' Jay tapped Felicia's perfect little posterior as she passed him. 'But quickly, eh?'

'*Sí, sí*. I no keep you waiting.' Again that little giggle!

No, I just bet you wouldn't, Beth thought disgustedly as Felicia swept from the room in a swirl of flaring scarlet and long black hair, and then lowered her glance quickly as Jay's sharp green eyes fastened on her pale face.

'You are sure you do not wish to come? Mateo will be quite safe in Luis's care.' She forced herself to look into his eyes as coldly as she could, trying to read the motive behind his cool invitation. What did he want? A harem? She bit down angry words with fierce determination. She would *not* let this man get to her!

'No, thank you. I would prefer to stay with Mateo.'

Something flared hotly in the brilliant green as he stared at her and then he turned away with a gesture of irritated impatience, his face closed.

'As you wish.' His voice was icy. 'Inform Juana we shall not be back until the evening meal.' His tone implied that she was a servant to do his bidding and for a moment she could have hit him.

She concentrated on Mateo for the rest of the day, trying to make her time with him enjoyable and ignoring the bitter flashes of anger and hurt that put a hectic flush in her pale cheeks and caused her eyes to sparkle like diamonds.

Later that night, as she showered and changed for dinner, her stomach tightened as she saw the studio light flick on in the room opposite hers across the silent dusk-filled courtyard. They were back, then, after their day together. For a moment a vision of Jay and Felicia in a passionate, frenzied embrace jumped unbidden into her mind and then she thrust it away in savage repudiation. She didn't care what they did, she hated them both, hated them!

She waited until exactly eight o'clock before appearing in the dimly lit dining-room and, as she had expected, Jay and Felicia were there before her, the latter flushed and glowing and full of animated chatter.

'We have wonderful day.' Felicia smiled lingeringly at Jay as he poured both women a glass of wine. 'We too long apart, eh, Jay?' The Mexican girl was wearing a full-sleeved, tight dress of a subtle golden hue that made her clear olive skin shine like silk, and for a moment Beth felt horribly dull in her sleeveless white silk dress, unaware of the tantalising fragility it lent to her slim shape and the way the sheen of white turned her hair into a cloud of glowing silver, her eyes dark grey pools in the paleness of her skin.

Jay smiled abstractedly before turning to Beth and passing her the glass of wine, holding the glass a fraction longer than was necessary, which forced her to look up into his dark, vitally handsome face. 'You had an enjoyable day?' he asked softly, watching her with intent, narrowed eyes.

'Fine, thank you,' she lied quickly.

He stood looking down at her, his broad, well-muscled shoulders hiding Felicia from her gaze as he slowly put out his hand to her hair, almost as though he couldn't help himself. She stiffened instinctively, her eyes darkening, and saw the movement register in the sudden hardness of his face as he let his hand drop loosely to his side. 'Good.' The word was harsh and for the rest of the evening he barely glanced at her as she sat, silent and aloof, while Felicia used her whole range of feminine wiles to hold his attention in a sickening display.

I can't stand much more of this, Beth thought bitterly as Rosa came in with coffee at the end of the meal, watching as Jay responded to some sally by tapping Felicia laughingly on the end of her pert nose. There was an intimacy in every look and gesture she gave him, a hunger, a desire that must be clearly visible to the tall, dark man watching her so indulgently. How could he encourage her to be so brazen?

'You remember my birthday, Jay, my sixteenth birthday? When you punch Ramón on the nose?' Felicia had leant forward so that the allure of her generous cleavage was on full display to the dark gaze of the man opposite her. 'It funny, so funny.' She slanted a quick glance at Beth from lowered lashes to make sure she was listening. 'He only try to kiss me.'

'I don't think there is anything particularly funny in hitting a man,' Beth returned quietly as Jay remained silent.

'No?' Felicia pouted whimsically and then gave Jay the full benefit of her huge liquid brown eyes, fluttering her lashes slightly as she spoke. 'Maybe not the punch, no, but what funny is that I only see Jay ever, only Jay. The others...' she shrugged her slim shoulders eloquently '...they nothing, and Ramón he a boy.' She reached across and touched Jay's hand where it rested on his wine glass. 'Jay, he so fierce for me.'

Beth could feel the colour start at her toes and spread swiftly into every part of her body. She had never before seen such a blatant offering of one person to another in her life. Couldn't they at least wait until she had left the room? She looked straight at Jay but he seemed remarkably unaffected by Felicia's behaviour, merely smiling a lazy, enigmatic smile and leaning across the table to place a swift kiss on Felicia's full red lips.

'Ramón, a boy?' His voice was laughingly teasing. 'I seem to remember he was nearly as old as I was at the time, twenty-three at least, and you were remarkably innocent for sixteen. He needed to be put in his place.'

Felicia, innocent? Beth looked at them with naked disbelief on her face and then quickly veiled her expression as Jay caught her eye. The beautiful Mexican woman had been born knowledgeable in the ways of love—it was in every move she made and every expression in those come-hither eyes. 'If you'll excuse me?' She rose from the table, unable to take any more.

'What is it?' Jay's voice was icy cold. 'Another headache?'

'The English are no strong, Jay; their blood, it is thin.' Felicia's voice was a clever combination of sympathy for the hapless English underlined with a fierce pride in her own heritage and that in his.

Jay ignored her completely, his eyes fixed on Beth's white face. 'You will be recovered sufficiently to ride tomorrow morning,' he stated with soft menace. '*Sí?*'

'I don't know——'

'Oh, but I do.' Anger flared blackly across his face as he watched her, his eyes slits of cold green, and suddenly the vision of *el tigre* lying indolently along the hidden branch in her dream was stark and clear in front of her.

She stared at him as though he were a demon from hell itself, and he rose from his seat, walking across to her and taking her chin in his hand as he spoke softly, his words inaudible to anyone but themselves. 'You have made it clear how you viewed our little talk yesterday and your answer is written in your face for me to read. I do not know what it is that makes you hold me with such abhorrence, *pequeña*, whether it is this——' he touched his seared face fleetingly with a cool hand '—or some other thing I do not comprehend. Whatever, your opinion is no longer of any importance to me, but I will not tolerate this . . . avoidance of my company. You will be ready to ride tomorrow and all the other tomorrows until you leave this place. *Comprende*?'

'Yes, I understand.' The nausea had fled, replaced by quivering, hot anger. How dared he lecture her like this when he had been alone with Felicia all day, no doubt lapping up all the attention and sickening adoration? How dared he? How many women did it take to satisfy his enormous ego?

'Good.' The fury in his tight gaze had been replaced by a cruel disinterest that was biting in its coldness, and it was only with a tremendous effort that she found the strength to turn and walk out of the room with her head held high, conscious as she left of Felicia's glowering interest in the quiet tête-à-tête, the subtle irony of the moment stabbing into her heart like a thin-bladed knife.

CHAPTER SEVEN

THE next few days were a form of subtle torture for Beth that left her pale-faced and hollow-eyed as night after night she lay awake for hours in the quietness of her room. Without Mateo's company she couldn't have borne it. The small boy had changed almost out of recognition since she had come to the ranch, his impeccable manners and serious charm brightened by a wicked sense of humour that had her laughing even in her blackest moments. He was a delightful child, the real Mateo who had emerged like a butterfly from the chrysalis of confusion, fear and despair.

'Beth, I think you are really becoming a horsewoman now,' he told her gravely on the morning ride when Felicia had been at the ranch five days.

She turned to make a laughing comment at the compliment but in the process caught Felicia's eye, and the contempt and hate on the smooth, beautiful face froze any response she might have made. Mateo followed her gaze, his face puzzled, and then his eyes widened with understanding as he met the full force of Felicia's venom before she could collect herself sufficiently to don the sweetly synthetic mask she normally wore in the presence of the two Rojas males. With a defiant toss of her head the beautiful Mexican girl dug her heels into the horse's flanks and rode past them to join Jay at the head of the party, leaving Beth slightly shaken at being on the receiving end of such bitter hostility.

She saw Jay reach out and touch Felicia's face in welcome as she reached his side, saying something she couldn't catch but which made Felicia throw back her head in a low, delighted chuckle of sensual delight. Beth felt the burning anger in her cheeks and willed herself to show no emotion. It didn't matter what they did, she would *not* let it!

On Felicia's sixth morning at the ranch Beth decided that enough was enough. There was no way she was going to endure another morning ride with the sight of Felicia and Jay, side by side on their magnificent, huge mounts, billing and cooing at each other while she and Mateo trotted behind like the original gooseberries. If he wanted an audience for his lovemaking then he could call on someone else.

Rising early, her stomach knotted in a giant tangle, she walked along to the dining-room with measured, controlled steps that belied the turmoil within. As she had expected, Jay was alone, his eyes narrowing at her entrance. 'You are eager to ride this morning, Beth?' The trace of sarcasm in the velvet voice was not lost on her and gave her the courage to say what she intended.

'Not exactly. I have no wish to ride today.' She met his gaze squarely. 'I thought I would give it a miss, actually.'

'I see; that is what you thought?' His voice was soft and silky but she heard the thread of steel and forced herself to keep calm and casual, nodding nonchalantly in reply.

'You are unwell?'

'No,' she said evenly, 'do I have to be? Surely I can choose whether to ride or not. It's not a crime to miss a morning, is it?'

'It could be.' He reached across for the coffee-pot and poured himself a cup before continuing, his face thoughtful. 'Let us examine the situation,' he said coolly after a long, taut moment. 'You are being unreasonable, purely for the sake of being unreasonable, as far as I can ascertain, and you expect me to concede to your wilfulness for the momentary satisfaction this will afford you. You persist on hanging back on the rides like a sulky, spoilt child that needs a good spanking and——'

'That is not true and you know it,' she flung back heatedly. 'Mateo and I don't have a chance to get anywhere near you and Felicia. We've tried more than once but somehow Felicia's horse always manages to cut us off in some way, making it impossible——'

'Please do not blame your petulance on anyone else, Beth.' His voice was hard and cutting. 'Felicia has nothing to do with this. You avoided my company long before she came and you still persist in this behaviour. You disappear immediately after dinner, you resist all overtures of friendship from Felicia and you treat me like a leper!' The last words were fired like pistol shots and as her eyes opened wide at the harshness in his face she watched him catch himself and take a long, deep breath before taking several sips of the burning-hot coffee.

She poured herself a cup and sat down gingerly on a seat as far away from him as she could, biting her tongue to keep back the hot words of anger that were quivering on her lips. How dared he blame all this on her? Couldn't he see how Felicia was treating her, the lies and deceit? Was he completely blind? But love was blind. The old phrase suddenly spoke into her mind as clearly as though someone had said it. Felicia was beautiful, she had pure Spanish blood and she absolutely adored him. What man could resist such a combination?

The thought suddenly drained all the anger out of her, leaving her pale and shaken. She hated it here. Hated him, hated this fierce crazy country, everything!

'I do not understand why you feel this need to oppose me at every turn, but I will not tolerate it.' The words were quiet and steady and totally without heat, but they chilled her far more than the savage anger he had displayed a few minutes before. 'Can you give me a reason, one good reason, why you do not wish to join us this morning?

'No, I thought not.' He had waited for long moments for her to speak and now turned away with a gesture of irritation and annoyance that had her clenching her hands into tight fists of impotent rage.

She wanted to finish drinking her coffee, to be as cool as he was, but her hands were shaking so much that she didn't trust herself to pick up the cup. 'What is it, Beth?' Her eyes snapped up at the changed voice and she saw that he had moved to her side, his face dark and still. 'I sense that you have much sadness, here, deep inside.' He tapped his clenched fist against his chest. 'This is so, is it not?'

She couldn't move, dared not move, every instinct in her traitorous body urging her to fling herself on the very person who was tormenting her and sob out all her fears, all her burning pain, to ask for a comfort he couldn't give. The intensity of her emotion shocked her. She didn't recognise herself any more; she wanted to hate him, she despised his cruel male arrogance, and yet . . .

'Oh, Beth, you were not meant to go through the desert of life alone. How will you find the life-giving springs, the very things that make this walk worthwhile?' His voice was low and deep and like fire on her nerves as he reached out a hand and touched her smooth cheek in a soft caress. 'What am I going to do with you, *pequeña*?'

'*Buenos dias*.' Felicia's face was smiling as they turned to look at her, framed in the open doorway like a beautiful dark-eyed cat, her long black hair coiled on

top of her head in a plaited knot and her slim body quite
still, but as Jay acknowledged her greeting with a quick
smile and then turned to resume his seat the full force
of her eyes turned to Beth and there was pure, malignant
hatred in their dark depths. 'You thirsty?' She looked
at Beth carefully, her eyes veiled now that Jay was facing
them again, and her expression quite bland.

'Not particularly.' Beth looked the Mexican girl full
in the face, her mouth straight. Felicia had had things
her own way long enough. Her nerves were stretched to
breaking-point and suddenly her fear of a difficult confrontation and what Jay might think didn't matter any
more. She would take no more sly insults and cunning
manoeuvres that were making life virtually impossible
for the sake of peace. Jay assumed it was all her fault
anyway; she had nothing to lose now by meeting Felicia
head-on!

She knew instantly that her thoughts were mirrored
on her face, for she saw Felicia's hard eyes register both
surprise and confused anger, before her narrowed glance
swept to Jay and then back to Beth again.

Jay's gaze was tight on them both. He had clearly
noticed the exchange and for the first time his eyes held
a gleam of puzzlement, but then Mateo burst into the
room, his animated chatter and bright presence breaking
the tension and allowing Beth's breath to leave her body
in a long sigh. The moment had come and gone and was
lost but she had the feeling that the confrontation had
merely been postponed.

Felicia was quite silent for once as they left the stables.
Normally she engineered herself by Jay's side with Mateo
and Beth following on behind, but today Beth found
herself in front of the Mexican girl as she stopped her
spirited mount to adjust the saddle. She looked at Jay
in front of her. He controlled Tornado with one hand,

his touch gentle but firm, and his big, powerful body perfectly relaxed and seeming at one with the huge animal beneath him.

The four of them trotted along easily in the crystal-sharp air of the new day, the thud of the horses' hoofs and the cool morning breeze wonderfully soothing on her taut limbs. She found herself relaxing and realised, with a feeling of surprise, that Felicia's confused anger had set something free. She had been foolish to let Felicia rule the roost and there was no way she was letting the cruel, hard master of the Rojas empire make her a live scapegoat for his 'friend's' mischief. The harsh words of the morning had placed things back in perspective and she would do some harsh talking of her own once they were back at the hacienda.

About a mile or so into the ride she was aware of Felicia moving up behind her and drew Toltec slightly to one side to let the Mexican girl pass. She obviously wanted to resume her normal position next to Jay and Beth had no wish to be close to Tornado anyway. Much as she was coming to love the other horses Jay's stallion was a thing apart! She couldn't look at him without a shiver snaking down her spine.

'You enjoy ride, Beth?' Felicia's voice was as cold as ice just behind her and Beth nodded without speaking. Now what was Felicia up to? Whatever it was, she wanted none of it. She turned and smiled at Mateo, who was bringing up the rear, and he grinned back in reply. At the same moment as Toltec reared into the air with a furious whinny she thought she heard Felicia laugh, but with the sound the horse had made she couldn't be sure. And then Toltec was galloping, fast and free, past Jay and out madly in front of them all and she knew real gut-wrenching, paralysing fear for the first time in her life. She was going to die, she knew it. She hung on to the animal's neck for dear life, her legs clenched tight against its side, feeling herself slip more than once and just managing to right herself in time. The ground flew by in a green-brown whirl and any moment she expected to be thrown to meet it. She forgot everything Jay had so patiently taught her for just such an emergency which he had insisted would never happen; her one thought was to stay on the animal for as long as she could.

She knew there was a ravine coming up and she also knew that Toltec wouldn't stop. She would plunge down into its razor-sharp depths because the alternative of flinging herself off the horse's back was too horrific to consider. As Tornado drew alongside her, with Jay reaching over for the dangling reins, she wanted to tell him to leave her or the four of them would be lost, but her mouth, like her legs and arms, was frozen with fear.

Toltec was slowing but it wouldn't be in time. She saw Jay force Tornado across Toltec's face, the huge black stallion rearing in angry protest, and then Toltec drew to a shuddering stop feet away from the ravine, more in fear of Tornado than anything else.

Jay was off his horse in an instant to catch her as she collapsed against him, sliding off Toltec's shiny, wet back with her legs pure jelly and shaking uncontrollably, her mouth still drawn back from her teeth in a grimace of fear.

He was muttering feverishly in his native tongue as he held her against him and as the tremors that were sweeping his body registered in hers she looked up into his face to see that he was as white as a sheet, the scar on his cheek standing out vividly in angry protest. He was holding her so tight that for a moment she thought she would faint through lack of breath, and then, as he opened his eyes, which had been closed in agonising relief, he saw her looking up at him and forced a twisted

smile on to his lips. 'That was what you English call the
close shave, I think?' She was too shaken to form a co-
herent reply, merely leaning her head against his hard
chest as she took tiny gasps of air. Strangely she didn't
want to cry—the enormity of what could have happened
was too terrible for the relief of tears.

'She OK?' Felicia's voice was hard and brittle as she
strolled to their side after dismounting her horse in casual
indolence. Beth caught a swift glimpse of Mateo's
pinched grey face in the background as he cantered up
on Tabasco and then her eyes snapped back to Felicia
again as the Mexican girl spoke. 'Such a fuss! You pale
Englishwomen with the white hands and no heart—you
no ride the horse.' The tone was scathing.

She felt Jay stiffen against her and then his voice
ripped through the warming air like the cutting edge of
a blade. 'Felicia! Enough. I am ashamed of you.'

'Of me?' Felicia swung towards him, her great eyes
flashing sparks of venom. 'For what? I speak truth.'

'Beth has only just learnt to ride, as you know. I would
not expect of her that she could control the animal in
such a situation,' he said coldly, his green eyes as hard
as glass.

Mateo had reached her side now and flung himself at
her so that Jay encompassed the pair of them in his hold.
The small boy was racked with sobs and quite hysterical,
and as Beth's eyes met Jay's over his head the same
thought flashed through their minds. The incident had
brought back all the despair and anguish a child felt when
he was powerless to alter something that was out of his
control. For a few moments it was as though his parents
had died again. Immediately the need to reassure Mateo
superseded anything else and she hugged him close,
muttering endearments into his silky curls as she kissed
the top of his head. The sight of the three of them closely

entwined was too much for Felicia to take. She made a sound that was halfway between a snarl and a groan and moved a step nearer to them, her eyes narrowed into black slits. 'Mateo, he very upset. She no ride again. Is no fair.' For once she was too enraged to pretend and the undiluted hatred in her face was there for all to read.

Jay put Beth and Mateo from him, very gently, and took the step that brought him a breath away from the furious woman, and although she couldn't see his face Beth knew from the expression on Felicia's that it wasn't pleasant. 'If you cannot control your tongue I shall be forced to control it for you. You understand me?'

'Jay, do not say this.' Felicia put a slim hand out towards him but the iron body didn't respond by so much as a flicker. 'It for her. I think of her. She no safe on Toltec.'

As Mateo launched himself like a small, enraged animal to Jay's side Beth was concious of thinking, in a detached, rational manner, that she wouldn't be surprised at what happened next. Everything and everyone seemed to have gone quite mad. 'How can you say such a thing, Felicia?' The boy's high, childish treble was quivering with indignation. 'I saw you; I saw you do it. Now leave Beth alone.' His small hands were clenched fists at his side.

As all eyes turned to Mateo Beth saw Felicia's face turn a dull red. 'Poof!' She dismissed the child with a wave of her hand as she turned, with studied nonchalance, towards her horse.

'Just a moment.' Jay's voice was deadly as he gripped Felicia's arm in a punishing hold. 'What do you mean, Mateo?'

'The pin—one of the pins from her hair.' Mateo was gabbling now, realising that he had stirred a hornet's nest of unimagined proportions. 'She stuck it into Toltec's flank. I see her.'

'Felicia?' The one word chilled Beth's blood.

'I no do it. He make it up. No good.' She flapped her hands at Mateo, who held his ground, his small face as determined as a bulldog.

'I did not, Gran Jay. I saw her. I tell you the truth.' The conviction and unswerving resolution in Mateo's voice must have convinced Felicia that she was on a losing wicket because she suddenly turned and looked straight at Beth, her face anything but beautiful as she glared at her adversary.

'An' why not? She no good. No good for you.' Her gaze fastened on Jay's face. 'You think her nice, eh? You like?' There followed an outburst in Spanish that mercifully Beth did not understand but that brought Mateo moving to her side where he clasped her middle with his arms, his head buried in her stomach as Felicia's voice rose and fell.

She didn't understand the words Jay used to halt the vitriolic flow but she didn't need to as their pitiless, implacable content had Felicia falling at his feet, holding on to his legs as though she were a penitent seeking absolution. 'No, Jay, no...' There was something almost inhuman in his face as he thrust her aside, walking over to Beth without a backward glance as the Mexican girl all but crawled in the dust, her face desperate.

'Beth. You come away from this. Mateo, you will lead Toltec home.' As he lifted her to put her on Tornado's back he suddenly pulled her fiercely into him and held her tight for a long, heart-stopping moment, and then she was on Tornado's back and strangely feeling no fear as Jay sprang up behind her, his arm strong and protective and his body warm and comforting behind her. Quite when the feeling of comfort ended and the slow, throbbing ache of his nearness took over she wasn't sure, but she was soon conscious of each movement the horse took that brought them closer together for a second, his body rigid and taut behind her and his arm a band of steel that held her against him. The slow rhythm of the horse became painful ecstasy as she was held next to his pounding heart, and the quiet grasslands on which they travelled were blurred and unreal as she concentrated with all her might on not betraying the shivering that was threatening to take her over.

She didn't realise they had arrived back at the ranch until she heard Luis's voice calling in the background and Jay's barked reply. He handed her gently into Luis's arms, jumping down immediately and taking her from him, whereupon it seemed as though he was growling orders to a dozen different people as he strode with her towards the hacienda with Mateo trotting like an obedient puppy at his heels.

'Jay?' She looked up into his harsh, dark face as they neared the house and his expression softened for a moment as he saw the wide, dazed blackness of her eyes.

'It is all right, little one. You are in shock and it is no wonder. You will have something to make you sleep and when you awaken this will all be a bad dream. No more.' She could hardly tell him that it was the feel of his arms around her and the tender expression on that hard face that was causing her to feel dizzy with an emotion she couldn't name.

On entering the hacienda all was pandemonium for a few brief moments as he organised Juana and Rosa to take care of her, returning after they had settled her in bed with a hot herbal drink that was heavily laced with sedative. 'That is the most disgusting thing I have ever tasted in my life,' she protested after one sip, and he allowed a small smile to touch the severity of his face as he knelt down by her side.

'You will finish it, all of it,' he said quietly. 'It is a natural product and it will help you sleep, and please, Beth, just this one time, do as you are told with no argument. I really do not have the strength or the desire to scold you into obedience.'

Her eyes opened wide at the throb in his voice and she finished the drink quickly, without speaking. It really was absolutely foul. 'Good girl.' He touched her cheek lightly with his hand as he stood up again. 'You see, it is not so difficult, is it?' Quite what he was referring to she wasn't sure, but she was beginning to feel deliciously warm and very tired, and it was quite beyond her ability to keep her eyelids open another second.

When she awoke it was to find the room in a cool semi-darkness and with a start of surprise she realised she must have slept the day away. She glanced at her small clock by the side of the bed. Seven o'clock! Whatever had been in that drink was certainly potent. She grimaced at the nasty aftertaste it had left in her mouth and padded into the bathroom to clean her teeth.

I'm absolutely starving, she thought to herself as she stood under a warm shower, letting the cascading water bring her fully alive. It didn't seem quite fitting to feel so normal after what had happened but she suddenly realised she felt surprisingly well. She certainly hadn't slept so well in weeks!

'Señorita? You OK?' As she heard Rosa's anxious voice she hastily turned off the water and pulled a huge bath-towel round her before sticking her head out of the bathroom door.

'I'm fine, Rosa.' She gave a big smile to emphasise her words as Rosa's understanding of English was practically non-existent. 'No problem.' She pulled a towelling robe on as she spoke.

'*Sí, sí, señorita.*' Rosa nodded her head, grinning. 'Dinner, *sí*?'

'*Sí.*' Beth nodded enthusiastically. Well, at least now the rest of the household would know she was coming through to dinner at eight as usual. She would just have time to see if Mateo was still awake before she got ready.

The small boy was almost asleep as she poked her head round the half-open bedroom door but sat up immediately on catching sight of her, his face beaming. 'Are you all right, Beth, really?'

'Good as new.' She sat down on the bed and hugged him before persuading him to lie down again. 'Sleep now, and Mateo, thank you for looking out for me the way you did today.' She traced the smooth young face with one finger. 'It was good of you, darling; you could have kept quiet.'

'I might have if *you* had done something wrong, but not for Felicia,' he said with the devastating honesty of children. 'But you wouldn't do anything like that anyway. You would never hurt anyone.'

'Oh, Mateo, I do love you.' She hugged him close again as she kissed him, her eyes full of tender tears. There was something about this small Rojas that always touched her heart.

When she entered the dining-room half an hour later she saw that Felicia and Jay were already there, the latter leaning against a small bookcase as he drank a glass of wine, his handsome face closed and still, and Felicia perched miserably on the edge of an easy seat, her beautiful face sulky and her eyes downcast on the glass in her hand. She didn't acknowledge Beth's entrance by so much as the flicker of an eyelash.

'Beth.' Jay moved quickly to her side as her stomach turned over in a giant leap. She had been dreading this moment. He seemed to be able to tangle her emotions in such a way that she barely recognised herself any more, and his concern and tenderness earlier that day had confused her beyond rational thought. How could he behave so coldly to Felicia out there on the plains when the two of them hadn't been separated for more than a minute since the Mexican girl's arrival at the ranch? He had made it clear all week that Felicia meant a great deal to him and yet, just for a little while that morning, she could almost have believed . . . 'You are recovered?' He was looking down at her, his green eyes bright and glittering, and she forced a smile through her stiff lips as she met his gaze.

'I'm fine, thank you.' She glanced across at Felicia, whose head was still bent. 'I don't know what was in that drink but it seems to have worked wonders.'

'Good.' He smiled before walking across to the table and pouring her a glass of wine. 'It is an old remedy of my mother's and never fails to work.' He turned abruptly to Felicia before handing Beth the drink, his eyes glacial as they fastened on her dark head. 'I believe you have something to say to Beth, do you not?'

'I sorry.' Felicia raised her head with what was obviously a considerable effort and met Beth's eyes reluctantly.

'And?' Jay's voice was relentless.

Felicia's huge brown eyes flashed to Jay's face with a deep appeal glowing in their dark depths but Jay's features could have been set in stone, such was their lack of expression.

'I beg your forgiveness.' The words were a low monotone. 'It joke, very bad joke.'

Beth nodded and turned away quickly, sickened by the lack of remorse after what could have been a very serious accident. She had no doubt at all that the Mexican girl had intended to harm her and wondered if Jay thought the same. His next words indicated differently.

'Felicia is young and somewhat thoughtless, Beth; I hope that this can be an end to this unfortunate incident? She is leaving tomorrow and will not be visiting the ranch again for some time.'

And that was it? She felt a fierce anger rise in her at his words but simply nodded again as she sipped her glass of wine without raising her eyes. No reprisals? Nothing? Felicia obviously came first, second and third! She missed the pleading anguish in Felicia's eyes as they met Jay's after his statement, and the way his green eyes became as hard as diamonds as they stared at the beautiful face with a burning contempt in their glacial depths.

Dinner was a subdued affair and although Juana had excelled herself Beth found that she could have been eating sawdust. Her whole being was concentrated on the man opposite her, so much so that she started violently when he suddenly spoke, his voice thoughtful.

'I am taking Felicia home tomorrow after breakfast, Beth, and I would like you to accompany us, please. You will be ready at nine?'

'Me?' She looked at him in surprise, a small dart of anger turning her eyes dark. Why had she got to go? Couldn't he leave her alone? If he thought she was going to endure watching him give a touching farewell to the woman who so clearly dominated his thoughts he had got another think coming! 'I don't think so.'

'I have not made myself clear, it seems. I am telling you to come,' he said coldly, his eyes sweeping over her with that strange, cold fire in their depths.

For a moment hot, angry words hovered on her tongue but as their eyes clashed she bit them back. He still had the upper hand after all. She was his employee. He could send her back to England and away from Mateo at a moment's notice and she didn't doubt for a second that he was capable of such an action.

'I see. I'll be ready.' Her voice was as cold as his and as she rose from the table it took all her will-power to remain cool and remote from them both.

As she left the room she heard Felicia's low, husky voice begin talking immediately, but it was all in Spanish and she didn't understand a word although the sensual, pleading undertone was as old as time itself. She was asking him if he still loved her, if he still needed her. Well, she knew the answer to that.

When she awoke, hours later, the events of the previous day crowded in on her with bitter clarity. It was still early morning and as she drew back the thin curtains and opened the wooden shutters on to the courtyard the rich scents of hundreds of flowers crowded in on her, and the clear morning air was piercing in its newness. The night sky was giving way to the pink-tipped day and a cool breeze played gently through the waving palms and shiny green leaves of the fruit trees.

She didn't want to go to Guadalajara with Jay today. She tried to face what was bothering her but somehow it kept slipping away. She would not, *would not* allow herself to be frightened of this man. If she could endure her father's cold rages and cruel treatment of her mother then she could stand up to Jay's domination. She could walk away from *this* tyrant at any time. She ignored the fact that the emotion Jay inspired didn't exactly come under the heading of fear.

Mateo was more than a little put out that he couldn't accompany the adults on the trip, but after Beth had promised that he could treat the whole day as a holiday with no lessons he brightened up and disappeared to his beloved stables with a little skip to his step. Beth watched him go with a small smile playing round her lips; his precious horses were the cure for any ill.

The journey to Guadalajara was over quickly, which was a relief to all concerned. Felicia had not appeared at breakfast, and when she did later, at nine sharp, her face was stony and her tall, slender body stiff. Luis parked the helicopter close to where he had picked Beth up on the first day, and then transferred Felicia's luggage into the back of the waiting taxi before resuming his seat in the helicopter.

'Is Luis waiting here for us?' Beth asked in surprise. It was hot in the sun and Jay usually displayed more consideration for his employees.

'Luis is going back to the ranch,' Jay answered smoothly as he helped the women into the taxi, and Beth felt Felicia stiffen by her side.

'He is?' She looked at him in bewilderment. 'When is he coming back for us?' She hadn't anticipated spending a day in Felicia's company and the thought was unnerving.

'He is not,' Jay said abruptly as the taxi began a hair-raising drive through the crowded streets. 'I have a car garaged in town that I use now and again and we will return in that.'

'Oh, I see.' She didn't, but with Felicia sitting glowering in the corner of the car she really didn't feel up to any further questioning and, besides, it was taking all her breath to remain calm and lucid in view of the taxi driver's remarkable driving technique—or lack of it! From what she could make out one drove at the other vehicles in a crazy sort of dare until one vehicle swerved out of the way at the last moment, often with a mad honking of the horn and a screech of burning tyres. Fortunately the journey to Felicia's home was only a matter of minutes, but Beth felt she had aged in as many years by the time they drew up outside the tiny, colourful house covered with purple and red bougainvillaea and trailing jasmin and honeysuckle.

Felicia's mother turned out to be as unlike her daughter as it was possible to be, small, round and immensely fat with a huge, beaming smile and gentle brown eyes that smiled out at the world above plump red cheeks. Beth liked her immediately and the feeling seemed to be reciprocated as the little woman took her arm and ushered her into her home, her other arm linked in Jay's. She ignored her daughter completely. Beth had heard Jay speaking to her that morning on the telephone but he had cut the conversation short when she had appeared. It was obvious that the circumstances of Felicia's homecoming had been made clear to her mother, however, and it was also clear where the little woman's sympathies lay.

After the inevitable coffee Sofía invited Beth to see the small aviary that filled the tiny courtyard at the back of the house, and after pointing out a number of tiny brilliantly coloured birds she left her there to rejoin Jay and Felicia in the house. Beth stayed where she was, recognising that the small woman wanted to be alone with Jay and her daughter.

'Ready to leave?' Jay's deep, rich voice brought her out of the reverie she had fallen into all alone in the hot, sunny courtyard, the birds twittering and calling to each other in the soft, warm air and the steady drone of insects melodious as they visited the flower-covered walls.

'Now?' She looked up at him in surprise and then her expression froze as she noticed a very definite smudge of lipstick at the side of his mouth. His goodbye to Felicia had clearly been...warm. Her blood seethed.

'Now is as good a time as any.' He seemed in remarkably good spirits and for a moment the desire to hit him, hard, was uppermost. 'I wish to show you a small part of my country and I think you will find the market here in Guadalajara fascinating.' He smiled down at her, his eyes soft. 'There are many sights——'

'I don't want to go sightseeing with you, Jay,' she said coldly and clearly, glad that her voice was not betraying the angry tightening in her chest. 'I would prefer to go straight back to the ranch. Mateo——'

'Damn Mateo!' His voice was a snarl and he had drawn himself up and away from her, his face straightening into the harsh, austere lines she was used to. 'You can leave the boy's side for more than an hour! I am not prepared——'

What he was not prepared for she would never know as at that fraught moment Sofía reappeared, her bright brown eyes flashing from first one angry face to the other, and then fastening on the side of Jay's mouth.

'You are still here?' She smiled calmly as she walked across to Jay's side, her small fat shape looking even more incongruous against his tall, lean body. 'It is just as well—my farewell kiss has left its mark on you, my boy. We cannot have you showing Beth the city with another woman's seal on you, can we? Besides, that colour does not suit you at all.' She was trying for lightness and it worked. After a startled glance at Sofía Jay allowed her to wipe the lipstick from his mouth, his eyes rueful as they met Beth's. 'You go and enjoy now.'

She pushed them both to the door. 'It is only two minutes to the market.'

Beth could hardly believe the vibrant cauldron of pulsating energy and colour that met her eyes as they rounded a corner and came out on to a huge square. The market spilled over into the neighbouring streets and houses, exciting, vital, with every imaginable item the Mexican housewife might need. Indian women in voluminous ankle-length skirts, their black braided hair entwined with coloured ribbons, sat displaying their menfolk's catches of fish from the lake, tiny pyramids of limes, oranges, peppers and onions in front of their stalls and beautifully woven scarves and bags and embroidered sashes behind them.

Serapes and massive blankets hung in gently moving walls of colour and pattern across the pavements, with long-haired fleeces displayed beneath canvas awnings by bent old men. There were stalls for everything—water jars, sandals, ropes, baskets, incense and candles as well as one with tiny ceramic bird-whistles among the pots and pans. She forgot everything in her enchantment.

'Oh, I must have one of those.' She turned to Jay, who was just behind her, his tall frame towering over the other men present by a good few inches. 'For Mateo.'

'For your son? *Sí, señora*, very good.' The vendor smiled a black-toothed grin as he blew on one of the tiny whistles to demonstrate their effectiveness, and she was glad Jay was behind her as she blushed scarlet. 'You like?'

'*Sí.*' Jay placed some coins in the outstretched hand as Beth chose the whistle she wanted, her cheeks still burning as they strolled away. 'You would like to rest, *señora*?' His voice was dry with delighted amusement and she swung round to face him angrily, losing the import of what she was about to say as she noticed a curiously vulnerable expression in the sea-green eyes a second before the inevitable shutter came down to hide their expression from her. No, she was mistaken, she must have been.

'It's a bit hot,' she said slowly as they paused by a cascade of woven blankets. 'Perhaps a cup of coffee?'

He looked at her tightly as she stood, small, slender and silver-haired, against the brightly coloured material and brown-skinned women in the background, and shook his head gently as his eyes lingered on her paleness. 'You look like a beautiful white dove lost in a flock of strange birds.'

She eyed him warily, a vision of Felicia jumping unbidden into her mind. 'I'm not lost.' Her voice was stiff.

'Are you not?' She hesitated, unsure of how to reply, and he took her arm gently. 'Come. We will have a cup of coffee and then I will show you Guadalajara, or a tiny piece of it.' He led her along a wide upper balcony that ran along two sides of the main interior of the market where the stalls were located, and she saw that it was filled with countless small counter-type restaurants populated mostly by Mexicans with very few tourists to be seen. It was fast and busy and confusing.

'The food here is delicious and inexpensive but it is something of a crazy place, eh?' She nodded in bemused silence. The bustle was overwhelming but with a wonderful atmosphere. 'You would like to eat?' He touched her cheek gently and she jerked away.

'No, thank you,' she said quickly. 'Just coffee.'

As they sat drinking the cinnamon-flavoured brew, overlooking the mad activity below, she slanted a considering glance at him from under her lashes. He was sitting, apparently quite relaxed, his long legs stretched out in front of him and one brown hand resting on the table as he surveyed his fellow creatures. How had he said goodbye to Felicia? The thought had been nagging at her all day and now she let it have free rein. Had he taken the tall, slender, dark-skinned girl in his arms and whispered his goodbye in her ear, or had he kissed her— had that really been her lipstick on his mouth? Had he comforted her, reassuring her that soon the stranger in their midst with her foreign blood would be gone and then...?

'Now what is it that is bringing this frown to your face?' She looked up, startled, to find his exasperated eyes on her face. 'Why can you not just enjoy the moment?'

'I can think what I want,' she responded heatedly, and now a frown darkened *his* face.

'Why is it I am sure that your thoughts bode no good for me?' His frown deepened at the tell-tale flush to her cheeks and savage derision lit the dark face for a moment. 'I have been found wanting again? *Dios*!' He swept back the black hair from his forehead. 'Never has there been such a woman!'

'Look, you brought me here. I didn't ask to come.' She glared at him angrily. 'I would have been quite content to go back in the helicopter and——'

'But I—I would not be content with that.' He leant forward suddenly and took one of her hands, turning it over in the palm of his while his other hand stroked the base of her wrist softly. 'I want more, much more.' A little flame was glowing in those emerald eyes and there was something almost menacing in the bitter, brooding quality of his smile as he lifted her hand to kiss where his fingers had touched. 'You think you can escape me?'

'I don't know what you are talking about,' she said sharply as she snatched her hand away so suddenly that one of her nails caught his lips, drawing blood, Felicia's spectre there beside him. Any woman would do for him, she thought angrily, any time!

'Such a little wildcat.' His eyes were chips of green glass. 'How am I going to tame you, *pequeña*?'

'You're not.' She stared back at him defiantly but as he noticed her trembling his face softened, and he leant back in his seat again, a mocking smile curving the firm lips.

'It is written in the stars, Beth. You have no choice in the matter.'

She couldn't continue this battle of words because there was something deep inside which was causing a quivering which she knew would come through in her voice. She lowered her gaze to her cup and finished the coffee without another word, conscious all the time of his piercing eyes watching her.

'Now, a little—how you say—sightseeing?' He had pulled her up before she realised they were on the move again and now he kept hold of her hand as he led her out of the market. She was aware of people's eyes on them as they walked, the big, fiercely dark, handsome man and the small silvery haired English girl. What were they thinking? She had noticed during the morning more than one pair of female eyes linger on Jay's big, well-muscled frame and had taken a perverse pleasure that she was the one he was with. She was going mad, she decided suddenly. Yes, definitely, completely mad. She must be on her guard!

They did most of their exploring on foot in a city that abounded with trees, flowers and fountains. She found the cathedral, surrounded by its four plazas, quite amazing. The exterior reflected a combination of Gothic, Byzantine, Tuscan and still more changes of fashion, but the interior was magnificent and awe-inspiring. The fine *retablos*—especially the painting by the famous

Spanish artist Murillo, the *Assumption of the Virgin*—had her silent and solemn, and when at last Jay drew her away, remarking caustically that she had had enough culture for one day, she was unable to find the quick retort that his presence usually inspired. 'We will leave the rest until next time,' he remarked as they walked to the car with a wicked tilt to his head, waiting for her reaction with amused eyes.

'What next time?' She looked up at him defiantly. 'I am here to teach Mateo for a few more months and then I go home to England. I am not supposed to be on holiday.'

'Even a donkey, that most ill used of beasts, has the occasional day off,' he said softly.

'I'm not a donkey,' she protested angrily and he drew her into his side, his arm wrapped round her waist as he laughed softly against her hair even as she tried to shrug away from him.

'That you are not, my little well-bred mare. You are of the finest stock, worthy to mate with the most noble of aristocracy. Yes?' His voice was quivering with suppressed laughter.

'I don't like the turn this conversation is taking,' she said stiffly and as she heard him give one of his rare bellows of laughter she had to fight to stop the bubble of amusement from showing on her face. This was all just clever tactics, that was all.

They ate before starting back to the ranch at an elegant, quiet restaurant which was very welcome after the hot bustle of the day. Jay led her to the outdoor patio where they dined amid shady green foliage and brilliantly coloured tropical birds, the flashes of bright scarlet from the breasts of the cardinal bird vivid against the dark background. The lobster, covered with a thick sauce, was delicious, but Beth found that her appetite was failing her as the magic of the dusk-filled night reminded her that she was only a temporary visitor in this exotic land, and that once she left she would be swiftly forgotten.

She had half expected Jay to stop the car somewhere on the way home, but he did not, drawing up outside the hacienda after the long, dusty drive with a deep drawn-out sigh. 'Here you are, safe and well.' She glanced at him sharply to see his dark gaze fixed mockingly on her face. 'You did not expect to escape so easily?' He had read her mind again!

'That's ridiculous.' A flood of crimson stained her cheeks and he laughed softly, a touch of cruelty about his mouth.

'Of course it is. So you will have no objection in sharing a drink with me before we retire?'

The house was quiet and still as they entered, with a dim light illuminating the furniture in soft shadows. She went to sit down in one of the chairs but Jay patted the sofa as he walked across to the drinks cabinet. 'Here. Near me.' She hesitated for a split-second and then told herself not to be so foolish. There were plenty of people in the house and, besides, she would not allow him to think she was nervous of him.

'You would like wine or a soft drink?' he asked smoothly.

'Lemonade, please.' He filled a tall glass with Juana's delicious home-made lemonade and brought it over to her quietly, the ice chinking against the glass, carrying his own drink of brandy in his other hand.

As he sat down beside her she was breathtakingly aware of every line of his body, and as she held out her hand for the drink he placed them both on the small table at his side and without a word took her in his arms, his mouth descending on hers in a hungry, hard, fiery kiss that stopped her breath. She had been waiting for this all day with a mixture of anticipation and fear, and now that he was making love to her she was powerless to stop him as she had promised herself she would.

'Every second I have been with you I have been aching to do this.' His hands moved feverishly over her body, pulling her into him and backwards so that she was almost lying under him, his body crouched over hers in an agony of need. 'So near and yet so far from me, you are driving me mad, little one. I no longer know myself.'

His desire thrilled her at the same time as she knew she shouldn't respond, but almost of their own volition her hands moved up into his dark hair in an action she had wanted to do many times. As he felt her fingers entwined in his hair, pulling his head downwards to meet her lips, he gave a groan that was almost like a wild animal's, his hands searching and finding her small, firm breasts, moulding their soft contours and finding their peaks hard with passion.

She opened her eyes for a brief moment, to see his face, dark and tortured with passionate desire, just above hers, and felt her last shred of control slipping away. He wanted her; his body told her that. Maybe Felicia meant nothing, maybe——

'You are so beautiful, so different...' The words acted like a deluge of cold water and as she froze in his arms he sensed her withdrawal. Yes, she was different, different from all the girls who shared his Spanish blood with their brown skin and pure heritage. She was different, like *Karen*. Should she substitute the word 'different' for 'easy'? Did he think she was like Alfredo's wife? Ready and available for any man who wanted her? She was one of the hated English, after all.

'I must go.' As she slipped from under him she was aware that he had let her go too easily, making no effort

to persuade her to stay in his arms. Why should he
bother? He probably thought next time would do as well.
He had already told her that he could mould her to his
will as easily as a moth to a flame. She fled from the
room with her heart pounding and the magic of the day
destroyed, and as she left, in a whirl of blonde hair and
pale limbs, she didn't see him pound his fist against the
back of the sofa, his face racked with violent emotion.

Once in the safety of her room she sank on to the
floor by the bed in an agony of weeping. What was this
power over her that he seemed to command? She had
seen how he had flaunted his relationship with Felicia
over the last few days, and now that she was gone did
he really think she would just fall into his arms? Just
because she was here and Felicia wasn't?

But she had done just that, hadn't she? She felt sick
as she remembered his easy conquest of her senses.
Perhaps that was how all the women her father had
picked up and dropped had felt? Drawn by his domi-
nating power in spite of themselves? She shivered in self-
disgust. And her mother. She had seemed grateful that,
each time, he came home to her. Well, that wasn't for
her. She had seen what that sort of relationship did to
the innocent party. Her mother had been dead years
before she had died, a walking shell going through the
motions of living with no real purpose in her life. And
all because of a man.

She pounded her fists against the softness of the bed.
'Never. Never.' She whispered the words as a vow in the
quiet room. He was cruel and hard and dangerous. She
wouldn't forget it again.

CHAPTER EIGHT

THE next few days were painful in their normality. Beth rode with Jay and Mateo in the mornings, she taught her small charge his lessons until early afternoon, she endured the evening and its closeness to Jay as they shared dinner, and all the time her heart and mind were crying out in an agony of confusion that she didn't understand. The morning after their trip to Guadalajara Jay had been his normal arrogant, cool self, betraying little emotion in his dealings with her beyond a distant kind of gentleness. She didn't want more than that, she *didn't*, so why was it hurting her so much?

'Beth, Tabasco has hurt her leg.' Mateo's small face was tragic as she joined him and Jay in the stables for the morning ride on the fifth day, until Jay ruffled his hair in playful mockery.

'Two or three days and she will be quite well again. In the meantime you can ride Suna.'

'I can?' Mateo brightened up immediately. Suna was one of his favourites among the stallions.

'Tell Luis to get one of the men to change the saddle from Tabasco to Suna while I see to Tornado and Toltec,' Jay told Mateo, who immediately rushed off, his small face aglow.

'Isn't Suna rather big for Mateo?' Beth looked down the stable block to where the massive animal was surveying them through half-closed brown eyes. 'He can ride Toltec if you like.'

'Toltec is your mount,' Jay said shortly. 'Suna is quite docile, I assure you, and Mateo is a good horseman.'

'I know but——'

'Leave it, Beth.' She said no more, standing to one side while he saddled Toltec for her and then strode down the block to take care of Tornado. Diego, the young stable lad, came and moved Mateo's saddle over to Suna who, she had to admit, stood quite still while he did so, in spite of Diego's obvious unease at dealing with the big animal.

They were well into the ride when the accident happened but fortunately merely trotting at a steady pace, Jay having squashed the gallop he and Mateo usually enjoyed in view of the boy's unfamiliarity with his horse.

Mateo was just in front of Beth and behind Jay and as she saw his saddle begin to slip and the small boy try to right himself she called out to Jay, but it was too late. Mateo slid, in an undignified flailing of arms and legs, right into one of the thorny burr-covered bushes that dotted the plain, landing with a dull thud in the middle of the spiky mass.

His yell could have been heard for miles around but after the one cry the child was silent, gritting his teeth as Jay leapt off Tornado and lifted him, as gently as he could, out of the cruel-looking plant. As Jay stood him to his feet Beth gave a gasp of horror at the sight of the nasty little burrs that had embedded themselves into every available inch of flesh.

'Oh, darling . . .' She crouched down by Mateo's side and would have taken him into her arms except that there was nowhere she could hold that wouldn't cause the boy pain. 'My poor darling.' Fortunately the thick denim jeans Mateo wore had protected his legs apart from a few scratches, but his bare arms, neck and one cheek were covered with the vicious limpet balls.

'Mateo?' Jay too knelt by his small nephew and looked deep into the boy's wide, shocked eyes. 'These things

must be removed from your skin as soon as possible.
Every minute they are in your flesh they are causing more
inflammation but we can either do it now or immediately we get home with a more suitable instrument.' He
indicated the small, sharp penknife he held in his hand.
'This may hurt too much.'

'Now, Gran Jay.' Mateo was shaking with a combination of pain and shock. 'Get them off.'

'You will be brave, I know.' Jay's eyes were soft with
pity as the small body trembled, and she saw his green
eyes narrow at the task in front of him. As he flicked
open the blade and lifted a small arm she saw him hesitate
and run his tongue over his lower lip.

'It is OK.' Mateo reached out a tentative hand and
touched his uncle's dark face that was on a level with
his. 'It will not be so bad.'

'*Bravo*, little one.' Jay touched the cheek without the
burrs in a gentle caress that brought a lump to Beth's
throat and an ache to her heart. 'I am very proud of
you; I have been meaning to say this for some time. You
are a true Rojas, Mateo, and I love you very much. You
know this?' Mateo nodded, his liquid eyes tight on his
uncle's face with utter trust in their brown depths, and
Jay nodded in his turn, his face tender.

'Now we must begin.' Jay used the tiny penknife with
deft precision, never pricking the reddened, swollen skin
but gently prising underneath the small, spiky burrs and
levering them out quickly. In a few minutes it was done
and as Beth hugged the child close Mateo sighed deeply
in relief.

'You were excellent, Mateo. Now we must get you back
to the hacienda and treat those wounds.' He turned to
Beth, his eyes glittering with rage. 'And I will deal with
Diego.'

'He's young, Jay, and——'

'He is also without a job. Such criminal care-lessness...' It was the first time she had seen him so enraged that he was at a loss for words.

He lifted Mateo in front of him on Tornado with an arm lightly round the boy, Suna, like the well-trained animal he was, falling into step behind them. Halfway home Jay slanted a quick glance at Beth to one side of him, his eyes a deep jade-green. 'The last time was more...enjoyable.' She knew exactly what he meant and as she remembered the feel of his big, powerful body holding her close as the horse moved beneath them she blushed furiously. Trust him to remember! 'There are so few women who do that any more,' he said musingly. 'I find it most attractive.'

'I'm glad I can oblige,' she said tartly, her expression losing its fire as she glanced at Mateo's white face. 'He'll be all right?' The child looked dazed and shocked.

'The burrs secrete a kind of poison, very much like a bee sting,' Jay said quietly. 'It is not dangerous but most painful for a few hours and in the number in which Mateo has them will make him ache all over. We have some ointment at home which will alleviate the worst of the irritation and a light sedative should help him sleep. He will be quite recovered tomorrow, eh, *niño*?'

Mateo nodded slowly, the cheek covered with the small sores red and angry. 'Can I still ride Suna tomorrow?'

Jay hugged the boy to him for a brief moment, his face twisting with pain. 'You can ride any horse you want to, little one. Your father would have been very proud of you today.'

'Like you?'

'Like me.' Jay's voice was gruff.

'You are sort of my father now, aren't you, Uncle Jay?' It was the first time Beth had heard Mateo call Jay 'Uncle' and, judging by the stunned look on Jay's face, the first time he had heard it too. She wouldn't have expected such a thing to cause the naked pleasure portrayed on the dark features, and glanced away quickly, her heart thudding. He was such a mystery, this man. One minute so ruthlessly fierce and the next full of compassion and gentleness. Maybe that was why she loved him so.

As the thought hit her brain she barely heard Jay's reply to the child, her whole being torn with this truth that she had been avoiding for days, weeks. Not him! Her mind was crying out against the knowledge in desperate repudiation. Of all people, not him—this cold, dark, savage man whose will was made of iron and just as relentlessly hard if challenged. But who could display a softness, a tenderness with anything small and weak that was magnificent in its compassion, her heart reminded her slyly. Whose devotion to those looking to him for protection was unequalled in her experience, and whose loyalty to his family was——

No! For a second she thought she had screamed the word out loud but a swift glance at Jay assured her that she had not. They were still trotting slowly across the vast plain towards the ranch, the morning sun gathering heat with every step they took and Mateo's small body held securely against his bulk. She couldn't love him, *wouldn't*!

'Do not be concerned, Beth.' She saw that his green gaze was fixed on her face and tried to school her features into order. 'He will soon be—how you say—as right as snow?'

'As right as rain.' She answered automatically, her face straight, and now his eyes were searching hers as he noted the distress turning her mouth white.

'*Sí.*' There was deep puzzlement in his dark face as they neared the hacienda and she felt that he sensed her confusion without knowing the reason why. She had never met anyone as perceptive as him and that fact alone frightened her. She would have to get away as soon as she could, leave this place forever, and in the meantime stay out of his way as far as she could if she was to leave this place with her mind and soul intact. How could she be so stupid? As they reached the ranch and went through all the motions of caring for Mateo her mind was functioning somewhere else. His contempt for Karen and her English blood that had contaminated his small nephew was one thing, and when added to his obvious affection for Felicia that hadn't, however, stopped him trying to seduce her—well, the conclusion was unmistakable.

The rest of the day dragged by and when evening came she was still sitting by the side of Mateo's bed while the child slept, her mind stunned and her eyes blank. 'This is taking the devotion too far, I think.' She raised heavy eyes to Jay standing in the doorway and noted, with a part of her mind that was still functioning quite normally, that he looked incredibly, vitally handsome. 'Juana informs me you have been here most of the day and that you barely touched your lunch. You will come now and eat dinner. He will not wake till morning.'

When she rose without a word and walked past him towards the dining-room his eyes narrowed thoughtfully, but he followed her silently, making no attempt to engage her in conversation as they ate the evening meal, although his hawk-like gaze was aware of every expression, every movement she made.

'I'm going to bed now.' Her eyes had a curious deadness to them as she finished her coffee and rose from the table, and still that whiteness had not cleared from her lips.

'Is there anything wrong? Anything you wish to share with me?' He moved to touch her hand but as she flinched from him he settled back in his seat, a darkness filling his face that would have intimidated her once, but now she was beyond that, beyond feeling anything except this huge, empty hole where her heart had been.

'No.' She looked at him without smiling and inclined her head politely. 'That was a lovely meal, thank you.'

'Mateo will be quite recovered in the morning.'

'Yes, I know,' she said flatly. She had to get away to her room before this comforting anaesthetic wore off.

'Beth... Come and sit with me, talk to me, tell me what it is that makes you so sad.' His face was quiet and still but still she shrank from it.

'No. I don't want to do that.' She looked at him with something akin to disgust in her eyes but he was not to know that it was directed solely at herself. 'I'm going to bed.'

'Then go!' he bit out savagely, his voice hard. 'I lose my patience with you. You act like a child.'

'Maybe.' Again her lack of reaction caused him to become still but she turned and left before he could speak, a small, ethereal shadow in the colourful, vitally male room.

It was three nights later when Jay's patience was finally exhausted. Beth had crept about the hacienda like a slim, silent ghost when he was present, although he had heard her laugh, once or twice, when she had thought she was alone with Mateo—but even that was a curiously cheerless sound.

'We will have coffee in the courtyard, Rosa.' Her eyes snapped on to his face as he directed the small maid in a quiet voice and she saw that although he spoke to the little Mexican girl he was looking straight at her. 'That is acceptable to you?' His voice was mockingly cold and she knew, immediately, that he had known she had been trying to avoid him.

'I don't want any coffee, thank you.' She met his icy gaze fearlessly.

'Nevertheless you will accompany me into the courtyard.' There was a harsh impatience in his voice that had her face paling even as her temper, in ashes the last few days, flickered and glowed.

'Why?' She looked at him as coldly as she could.

'Because I want you to.' It was said with supreme arrogance and total disregard for her feelings in the matter. 'I am tired, more than tired, of your attitude the last few days, Beth. I want some answers and I want them now. I wait no longer!' The last words were a low snarl and as though in emphasis he took her arm in a cruel grip, almost dragging her along the corridor to the study where he opened the door leading on to the dimly lit courtyard and threw her down into a seat. 'You sit there. And no more this and that. You answer me. You answer me now!'

He loomed, dark and threatening in the shadows, and now his face was the face of the man she had first met, the man who had disgusted and alarmed her with his coldness and his pride, and she found that it was easy to respond to that cruel stranger.

'You can take a horse to water but you can't make it drink!' She heard herself say the trite words with a feeling of amazement considering the gravity of the situation, and then Rosa appeared with the tray of coffee, her small round face wide-eyed as she sensed the tension between them.

'*Gracias*.' The word was a dismissal in itself and the little maid scurried away as fast as her legs could carry her. 'Now, what is this horse drinking?' The ice-cold voice was bitterly contemptuous as he stood in front of her, hands on hips and legs slightly apart. 'You talk rubbish. You can do better than that.'

'How dare you?' She rose to face him, her dark eyes flashing fire now. 'I won't have you talk to me like this.'

'You will not?' He pushed her down on the seat as he bent his body to join her. 'You will not have it?'

'No.' She spat the word at him.

'But I am expected to endure your unreasonable behaviour without comment, eh? This running away, this treatment that I am the monster?'

She stared at him angrily. 'Don't you dare touch me again and I haven't said——'

'No, you have not said!' he interrupted her harshly. 'You never say. You merely look at me with those big grey eyes and I can see that there is the disapproval in your heart. I have taken more from you than I ever expected to endure from a woman and still you are taking me to the limit. Well, this is too much!' He pulled her against him so violently that her head snapped back on her shoulders and then he was kissing her, angrily, fiercely, with no shred of tenderness or affection. The embrace was a bruising, painful punishment and mirrored the rawness of his emotions more than any words could have done.

She fought him at first, silently and wildly, but then as his strength dominated her struggles she was horrified to find that even in his rage he caused insidious little flickers of desire to snake down her spine. She loved him. He must never know but that was why his touch melted her resistance more effectively than any physical force. She suddenly knew that it was too dangerous for her to stay here any longer. She would have to leave, leave the ranch and him and...Mateo? Her heart cried out in protest even as her mind told her there was no other way.

'In spite of your disgust I can make you want me, can I not?' He raised his head for a moment to look down into her dazed eyes. 'You need me, Beth, as much as I need you.'

'No.' It was a weak denial and his eyes flashed that cold fire as their brilliant green raked over her face.

'But yes. You do not like me, do not like this desire that makes your body burn, but you want me to hold you in my arms and satisfy this torture that makes you hide from me. Do not deny it. Your heart may be cold but your body is not.'

'No!' Even as she denied him he covered her mouth with his own, his hands and his mouth working together to render her quivering and helpless within minutes. She knew that he had opened her blouse as the cool night air shivered on her hot skin, but she was powerless to stop him, lost in such a whirlwind of yearning passion that she no longer recognised herself.

'This, this is the finale, Beth.' As he stood up away from her she looked up into his dark, harsh face in weak confusion, aware of her state of undress but too dazed to move. 'I will not become the fool for you, no matter how much I——' He stopped abruptly, his face a black, satanic mask. 'I will not bother you again. You have my word, as head of the Rojas family, on that. I give you the solitary walk, the isolation that is so important to you.'

'Jay?' She was seeing yet another side to the complex personality of this man she had grown to love. Cruel, savage pride turned the handsome face into hard bronze, the pale silver thread of the scar the only indication that she was looking at a human being who could love and suffer loss. There was a blank coldness, a distant remoteness deep in his eyes that alienated her, totally and forever, from the harbour of his arms. He meant every word he had said. She knew it.

'You want me to leave?' He had grown tired of her; maybe she even disgusted him with her pale skin and fair hair so like that of his brother's wife who had been the instrument of tearing their family in two?

'That is your decision, Beth.'

'Then I'll go.' She stifled a sob with sheer will-power. His voice had been so hard. 'Will you make the arrangements for me? I don't understand Spanish and——'

'I will see to it.' He looked down at her for a long, still moment, his eyes moving over every feature of her face as though trying to imprint them on his mind, and then he turned and was gone without another word.

How she got to her room without breaking down completely she didn't know, but she moved as though sleepwalking, her face as white as a sheet and her heart pounding. This was it, then. It had all really finished, abruptly, unexpectedly, like this. How soon would she go? Would it be tomorrow, maybe without seeing him again, or the next day perhaps? What did it matter? She shook her head wildly. She was going, wasn't she? He didn't want her here any more. But Mateo—how would he take her sudden departure? Her heart felt as though it was splintered into a hundred pieces and for a moment Mateo only was in her mind.

She would have to reassure him of her love, promise him that she would be waiting for him in England when he arrived. It was only a few months after all, and she could write to him. He would still be at the ranch, still be with the horses he loved so much. Those thoughts didn't help to assuage the guilt she felt.

After three hours of tossing and turning she crept out into the courtyard from her room, a dark silhouette treading silently on bare feet. The night sky was a thick black blanket of tiny twinkling stars, scents of hibiscus, jacaranda and a hundred other exotic plants heavy in the cool air. She sat trying to accept the inevitable as time ground relentlessly on. Soon she would be gone, gone from this strange, beautiful land she had come to love, never more to see the sharp, pointed blue-grey maguey plants forming protective hedges around small fields of maize and corn, the wandering goats and cattle strolling aimlessly across dusty lanes and green fields, grizzled, dour-faced old men minding their small flocks in the fierce noonday sun...

She forced her clenched fists into her eyes as she tried to blot out the vivid pictures in her mind. This new world, with its distinct contrasts of teeming city life and vast open plains, had found a place in her heart only because of him. If only... If only what? Her heart cried out to her in harsh challenge. If there were no Felicia, and had been no Karen to sour his view of English women, what then? She knew, deep in that hidden recess in her heart, that her father had blighted her for life. She would never have the courage to trust fully a member of the male species. Even if he had loved her she couldn't have stayed, would never be able to stay anywhere where there was an element of commitment to any one man—especially a man like him.

Strangely the thought emptied her heart and left her calm and lifeless, and when some time later she crept into her room and lay down she was asleep within minutes, utterly exhausted.

'Beth, it is not true!' Mateo woke her the next morning from a deep, dreamless sleep, his face pale with distress and his eyes huge. 'Gran Jay says you have to leave. Why do you have to go?'

As Beth raised herself dazedly in the bed she reached out and pulled the small, taut body to her side, biting her lip as she realised that Jay hadn't wasted any time in informing his nephew of her decision. He clearly couldn't wait to see the back of her. The thought was unpleasant but she fastened on it, trying to force some anger into the deadness of her mind.

'I have to go, Mateo,' she said gently as she looked deep into the soft brown eyes fastened on hers. 'I don't want to leave you but I have to go—but it needn't be goodbye. I will be waiting for you when you come to England and I'll come and see you at your school, I promise. We can——'

'But I'm not going to school in England.' Mateo looked at her in some confusion. 'Hasn't Gran Jay told you?'

'Told me what?' Beth asked slowly.

'The night Firebrand was born—that night, Gran Jay said I could stay in Mexico if I wanted to, that I did not have to go to England to school.'

'You aren't to be educated in England?' Beth stared at him in amazement. 'But why didn't your uncle tell me? Why did I continue here if not to prepare you for England?'

'I do not know.' Mateo looked at her solemnly. 'I did not know he had not told you, Beth. I don't think it was a secret.' He wrinkled his smooth little brow. 'Perhaps he liked to have you here—I know I do.'

'I know you do.' Beth cuddled him close as she searched her mind for a reason for Jay's action, but then Mateo claimed her attention again.

'Can I come and see you in England still? Have a holiday with you?' he asked anxiously, his eyes suspiciously bright.

'Of course you can.' She smiled at him lovingly. 'I'm sure your uncle will agree to that—he knows I will look after you properly; but I just can't stay here any more. Gran Jay and I just don't get on, Mateo, and it's making him cross and me unhappy for me to stay. Try to understand.' She pushed him away slightly to look hard into his eyes. 'I don't want to leave you, there is nothing I hate more, but I have to go.'

'So you really are leaving?' Mateo looked at her with defeat written across his face. 'You will not change your mind?'

'I can't, darling.' As he flung himself into her arms she knew a moment's piercing pain as deep as any mother experienced when leaving her child, and then he was racing out of the door. She instinctively knew that it was because he didn't want her to see him crying, and that hurt still more. He was growing up so fast and yet was still such a child; he needed so much love.

Once alone she mulled over Mateo's revelation. So Jay had had no intention for weeks of sending his nephew to England? Then why hadn't he dismissed her and employed a Spanish tutor who would be biddable and problem-free? It didn't make sense. She pulled out her suitcases and began to pack slowly. It must be because he had realised how attached Mateo was to her, that psychologically it had been better for the boy for her to remain here until he was emotionally settled. She remembered his words from the interview all those months ago. 'My first concern must be for Mateo.' Yes, that would be it. How her presence must have irritated him, especially after all the trouble with Felicia.

There was a deep, bottomless blackness settling on her spirit that she had never experienced before and she felt too weary to fight to rise above it. Apart from this strange physical chemistry between them they were worlds apart in everything that mattered, and now he seemed to have mastered even that temporary weakness.

She didn't touch that black heart at all. Why had she ever come to this place? And, once here, why had she stayed? Mateo's small face swam before her and she bit her lip, fighting back the tears that once released would have no end.

In that moment she reached total rock-bottom and knew, for the first time in her life, how terribly alone a human soul was capable of feeling.

CHAPTER NINE

IT WAS only ten minutes later when Mateo returned, his eyes red-rimmed but outwardly composed, and she was immensely relieved to see him. For once she was desperate not to be alone. The child informed her that Jay had gone into Guadalajara for the day on business and that he had arranged a place for her on a flight to England before he had left. 'It is for tomorrow.' Mateo's face was bleak. 'This is your last day here, Beth.' Her heart stopped to then race furiously at the finality in the words.

'Then we will spend it together doing what you want,' she said gently as she knelt to take his stiff little body into her arms.

It was in the half-hour before Mateo's bedtime, when he was helping her to finish the last of her packing, which had been abandoned for the day, that the small boy came across her much treasured photograph of Samantha, taken on her birthday a few weeks before the little girl died. 'Who is this?' Mateo looked at the child in the wheelchair smiling with unaffected delight into the camera.

'This is the little girl I looked after before I came here,' Beth said carefully, glancing at the photograph with the usual wrench to her heart. Samantha's bright face grinned back.

'Why is she in a wheelchair and what is the matter with her face?' Mateo looked up at Beth, his brown eyes troubled.

'She had a disease, Mateo.' Beth knelt down and took his hands in hers. 'She was very brave and very happy but she didn't get better. The treatment they gave her made her look like that.'

'Oh.' He looked at her seriously. 'Was she pretty once?'

'She was always pretty, Mateo, before and after,' Beth said quickly. 'What was inside her made her beautiful and she was always the most lovely little girl in the world to me. What shows on the outside doesn't matter at all; this thing we call a body is just a shell, and houses the most important thing—the thing that makes you you. It's called your soul and Samantha's was strong and loving and caring. She is in heaven now and very happy.'

'Is she?' He sounded doubtful.

'Yes, she is,' Beth said firmly. 'I know she is.'

'Good.' His face said quite clearly that if Beth said it was so, it was so. He changed the subject completely in the mercurial manner peculiar to him, and after they had finished the packing Beth oversaw his bath and then tucked him up in bed, enduring a few poignant, tearful moments on both sides, before she went along to her room to change for dinner.

She was unaware that Jay had returned home until she heard his unmistakable sharp knock on her door. For a moment she contemplated pretending she wasn't there and then the absurdity of the idea hit her and she walked slowly to the door, her stomach churning. 'Good evening; I'm ready for dinner.'

'Damn dinner!' She took a step backwards as he spoke, noting the white line round his mouth and the strangely stricken expression in the clear green eyes. He looked as though he had been punched very hard in the stomach, which, if she thought about it, was exactly how she had felt for the last twenty-four hours.

'I have been to say goodnight to Mateo.' It was as though his words were some sort of explanation, and she stared at him blankly.

'Have you?'

'He told me what you said.' There was a curious note in his voice that she couldn't define, and she wondered, for a fleeting moment, what new charge was being laid at her door.

'I'm sorry, I don't understand.' She stared at him standing white and still in the doorway. 'You had better come in for a moment.'

He strode into the room in his usual swiftly arrogant way but walked almost in a circle before he stopped, as though his mind was elsewhere. 'About the child you cared for before you came here. Mateo told me what you said to him.'

'Samantha?' She tried to remember the import of her words to Mateo but couldn't find anything in them that would cause the hunted expression on Jay's face. He stood facing her now, his tall, powerfully muscled body completely still and his head thrown back as he stared into her soft grey eyes.

'Mateo said the child in the photograph was ill, disfigured, but that you insisted she was beautiful.'

'She was.' Beth looked him straight in the eyes, her face speaking for itself. 'If you had known her——'

'Then why, *pequeña*, why?' There was a bitter, dark rage about him that she didn't understand and was powerless to comprehend. 'Why is it that you can love a child like that, without reserve and with all your heart, and yet you find me...repulsive?' He touched his marred face for a second, his eyes proud and cold.

'I don't.' She stared at him in horror. 'Is that what you think? I don't, Jay, truly.' The rigid expression on his face told her she wasn't reaching him.

'Is it only children that touch this heart of ice?' He rested his hand for a moment on her breast and it burnt like fire. 'I am too old for this understanding?'

'You don't understand, Jay.' What did he want of her, a total subjection? 'I have never considered physical appearance important whether in children or adults—believe it or not.'

'I choose not.' His voice was cold and his face stiff.

She looked at him for a long moment and then shook her head dispiritedly. 'Oh, what does it matter anyway? Felicia adores you, and she is so beautiful. When you marry her——'

'Marry Felicia?' He stared at her as though she were deranged. 'What is this? Did Felicia tell you I intend to marry her?' His tone caught her on the raw and she flushed angrily.

'No.' She waved her hand in the air. 'But there are some things that are clear without words. She loves you so much and——'

'And I? Jay de Rojas? I have no say in this matter?' He glared at her angrily. 'You think I desire Felicia as my bride?'

'Don't you?' She glared back as she spoke. 'I can understand it, Jay; she is so beautiful and——'

'Stop this beautiful, beautiful!' he bit out impatiently. 'Felicia is like the little sister I never had and I care for her like a sister. That is all. Not the way I care for you, my Beth . . .'

'Me?' She couldn't have heard right, she thought wildly.

'Of course. Why do you think I have endured such wilfulness from a female if not through love? From the moment I lifted you into my arms when your eyes were closed and your head laid back, exposing your throat like a slender, broken lily. . . *Dios*!' He turned full circle on his heel, his eyes brilliant with rage. 'From that moment I forgave Alfredo for his weakness because for the first time I could understand my brother. He lived, breathed his Karen, and my being has not been at rest since I met you.'

'But Jay...'

'I know, I know. The Rojas line is fated with unrequited love. My grandmother adored my grandfather but he had no time for her and then Alfredo was destroyed by his obsession with his wife. And now you, my pure little English rose. You too have worked your way into my heart with your thorns embedded deep in my soul, the thorns of hate——'

'I don't hate you, Jay.' She knew her heart was breaking, because the pain was so intense as to be unbearable. 'Please listen to me; I don't hate you.' Oh, to cause the one she loved such agony—she would carry this moment with her to the grave! It was worse, much worse, than the belief that he had never loved her. Now she would suffer the consequences of her cowardice forever, the knowledge that she did not have the courage to reach out for something in her grasp.

'Beth.' Her name was a prayer on his lips and she read in his eyes that he had recognised her anguish. 'Then why, Beth, why? There is nothing to stop us if what your heart is telling mine is the truth.'

'No!' She jerked away when he would have taken her in his arms, her voice full of panic and her face stricken. 'Please go, just go.'

'Go?' His voice was a throb of triumph. 'How can you ask this of me?'

'Because I can't, *won't* stay here. Now more than ever I have to go.' She turned her face away, white and shaking.

'I do not understand this "won't"—explain.' She sensed that he had no intention of leaving unless she convinced him there was no hope. 'I will not rush you, little one. I understand that you have not known a man before and that the ways of love are strange to you. I want you as my wife, Beth, and in this thing I can be patient.'

'I do not trust you, Jay.' As she spoke she saw the hard pride sear his face in angry red colour. 'I do not trust any man.'

'Any man?' He shook his head impatiently. 'Again you make no sense. What is this thing you are telling me?'

'Please, I can't explain, Jay. I just cannot be what you want. There is no future for us and——'

'How can you say that?' As he took her in his arms she knew that if she let him make love to her she would be lost, and as her eyes widened with the shock of what she was about to do she drew back her hand and hit him across one tanned cheek as hard as she possibly could.

'Is that plain enough for you?' She could hear her voice shrill and ugly but her control had finally snapped. 'I won't be yours, yours or any man's. I am a person in my own right and I can't let you control me. I hate you, do you hear me? Go away, just go.' As he stood in stunned silence she ran to the bed and threw herself down in a tempest of weeping, and as she heard the door click to and raised her streaming eyes it was to survey an empty room. He had gone. That last blow to his pride had been final—she had known it would be, but she had had no other choice. A life without him was terrible to consider but a life as his wife, under his domination and with the slow loss of her identity, was not to be borne. She had seen it happen to her mother, and nothing, nothing was worse than that.

She awoke the next morning feeling sick and ill with lack of sleep and the dreams that had oppressed her when she had finally dozed. Had she done the right thing? The thought was beating a painful rhythm in her head. She didn't know any more. For twenty-five years she had been sure of what she wanted and, more especially, what she didn't want. Now this green-eyed stranger with his proud, autocratic manner and overbearing darkness had turned her safe little world upside-down. Still, it was too late now. He would never forgive her for rejecting him so savagely. She knew that. That was why she had done it. A final burning of all the bridges.

'Beth?' The small knock at the door and Mateo's high voice brought her back to herself, and as she struggled to lighten the next hour or so for the child she managed to keep the anguish and hopelessness from swamping her.

They ate breakfast alone; Jay seemed to have vanished from the face of the earth, and Juana informed her, with a little catch in her voice and her brown eyes full of tears, that the *señor* had given Luis all her papers and instructions for the airport. He wasn't even going to say goodbye, then?

'We will say farewell here, Mateo.' Beth knelt down in the hall as Juana and Rosa carried out her bags, and took the shaking little body in her arms. 'It will only be for a while, I promise. Your uncle will let you come and see me.' Please let that be true, she prayed silently as the small arms snaked round her neck in a tight bear-hug. As two big tears squeezed out of his eyes Mateo made a dash for his room after a muttered goodbye, and Beth stood up slowly, her head buzzing. This was her fault, all her fault. She couldn't bear this.

'Your cases are in the helicopter, *señorita.*' Juana's face held a slightly puzzled expression although Beth didn't know why. *'Hasta la vista.'*

'I'm sorry, I don't understand.' Beth had not heard the phrase before.

'Till we meet again, *señorita.*' The small housekeeper stepped forward and hugged her to her ample bosom for a brief moment.

'Adios, señorita.' Rosa's small face was straight for once, and that brought home the fact more than anything else that she was really leaving that morning.

'Adios.' As she walked to the helicopter her eyes were blinded with tears, and as she felt someone help her into the whirring machine she wiped her hand across her eyes as she strove for control. *'Gracias.'* As her vision cleared she saw that she was looking down into Luis's concerned face and her glance flashed in bewilderment to the figure beside her at the controls. If Luis was on the ground, then who...?

'Buenos dias, Beth. Do not make any attempt to leave this vehicle because I will tie you in the seat if necessary.' Jay's deep, velvet-smooth voice was brusque and cold.

'What are you doing?' She found that she was fighting for breath as though she had been running. 'Where are you taking me?'

'You want to leave, so you are leaving. A slight detour first, that is all.'

'You're crazy, mad...' She was trembling but couldn't help it.

'All of that and more,' he said grimly. 'However, do not concern yourself that I cannot fly this small machine. I obtained my pilot's licence some years ago and you will come to no harm.'

'I won't go with you; you can't——' As she went to open the door that Luis had shut he put his hand over hers, his face savage in its bitterness.

'I meant what I said, Beth. I will tie you in your seat. Do you not wish to leave this place with a little dignity?'

'If I try and get away Luis will help me, or Juana. They don't know what you're doing——'

'They value their well-being, Beth.' His voice was grimly determined. 'They would not lift a finger to help you and you would merely embarrass both yourself and them. Now fasten your seatbelt and behave yourself. I know you do not trust me, that you consider me little better than the guard-dogs that patrol my property, but I will not hurt you. You have my word on that.'

As the helicopter whirred into the hot blue sky she had an insane impulse to open the door and leap out, but it was only a fleeting madness born of a mixture of impotent rage, grief and desperate fear. They passed quickly over the plain below where small lizards skittered abruptly from their sunbathing on the scattered rocks as the noisy machine whirled overhead, and then he turned away from Guadalajara and out into a long, low valley rimmed in by rugged mountains on which large trees clung tenaciously, brightly coloured orchids and other strange succulent plants in their turn clinging to the trees. As Jay expertly landed the machine in the middle of a vast, grassy expanse of brown and green she waited, hands clasped tightly together, for him to speak.

As the noise died away a deep, silent quietness invaded the sleeping valley and it was as if they were the only people alive in all the world. 'It is said that tears are the rainbow of the soul.' He touched her cheek gently as he spoke and she was surprised to see that his hand was wet with her tears. She hadn't even realised she was crying.

'What do you want of me, Jay?' She looked at him pleadingly. 'This is hurting me.'

'We're hurting each other, *pequeña*, and it has gone on too long. I will not move from here until you tell me what it is in your life that has caused this fear, this sorrow. You were made to fly like a white dove in the sky, not grovel on the ground like a wretched snake of the plains. If we have to sit here for days I will do it. I mean it, Beth.' The thread of steel she recognised. Maybe she should have told him before? Let him see that she was marred inside just as surely as his face held the memory of Alfredo's death?

He made no attempt to touch her and for that she was grateful. As she began to tell him about her father, the cruel womanising, rigid, petty rules and cold, heartless desire to reign supreme in his own little world, his face remained closed and shuttered. She detailed the ig-nominy of being the only child who was not allowed friends home or to go visiting, of his rages if her mother should serve a meal just a minute late, of the deliberate alienation of all her mother's relations and friends. 'I used to think he was a madman but then I found he wasn't,' she said quietly as she finished speaking. 'That was the worst thing to come to terms with. I could have understood it all if his mind had been unbalanced, but he was simply a male tyrant of the worst kind, a vile bully and a cruel taskmaster.'

'And you think I am like this man?' There was a deep, raw hurt in Jay's face. 'That I am capable of such behaviour?'

'No, I don't think that,' she said slowly, 'but how can I be sure? My mother told me once that he was quite different before they got married. I can't ever take that risk.'

'Kiss me, Beth.' He touched her lips with his finger. 'Let your senses tell you what your heart already knows: that you love me and I love you. I am not your father and you are not your mother. Whatever went wrong between them we shall never know, but you cannot, must not, let them ruin your life forever. This must be a new beginning for you.'

'I can't, Jay.' She looked at him with a searing anguish in her eyes. 'Don't you see, I can't?'

'No. I see nothing but you and you must see nothing but me.' As he kissed her his lips were gentle, a compassion, a deep tenderness reaching out to her that had not been there before. He nestled her into him, protective, loving, but careful not to use a shred of force to win her over. She could feel her head begin to swim, feel the relief, the blinding joy of being held close to him again work its magic. As he parted her lips and took the sweetness within she heard her tiny groan of delight as though it were someone else. She loved him, so much, so very much. She couldn't let him go again, not again. She had tried and she had lost. She would have to take what the future held.

'I love you, Jay.'

As she murmured her submission against his lips he moved her gently from him, his face quizzically sad. 'That is not enough, Beth. I do not only want your love. I want your trust.' She looked at him blankly. 'I trust you enough to make you the mother of my children and to share my life with you. I am greedy, Beth. I want it all. Only all is good enough.'

'I don't understand.' A cold shiver ran down her spine as she saw the determination on his handsome face.

'You have known me for many months now. If you marry me you will come under my protection as my wife and I would die to protect you, to keep you safe. My life will be yours but I must have yours in return. Perfect trust, Beth—for the decisions I make in the future that you may not understand, for the times when you may think me stern and unbending with those around me. I cannot be seen to be weak, *pequeña*. In return for this trust you will have mine also. I will love you, adore you as no woman has ever been adored.'

'And if I can't say I trust you like that?'

'Then I will take you to the airport now and never contact you again. I will live my life here, waiting, in case you should change your mind and return to me, but if you do not, then I will die an old man with no son to carry on my name. There will never be anyone else but you, my thorny English rose.'

He settled back in his seat as she looked down at her hands in her lap. 'To the airport or to the ranch. Whichever you choose, Beth. The decision is yours, *has* to be yours.'

As the minutes ticked by she kept her eyes lowered. He was so still, so silent that she couldn't even hear his breathing, and when she raised her head at last it was to see his face, his dark, handsome face, torn with love and awash with pain.

'I love you, my darling, and I can't leave you. I trust you, Jay. I give myself to you. The ranch, please.'

He was her destiny.

CHAPTER TEN

'I THINK I will always keep you as you are now.'

Beth looked up quickly from her contemplation of the heavy gold band on the third finger of her left hand that nestled close to the exquisite diamond solitaire next to it.

'Will you indeed?' Her grey eyes were filled with love as she watched her husband of eleven months and three days leave the adjoining bathroom, magnificently naked, and stroll with the lithe animal-like grace peculiar to him over to the bed.

'Yes, it pleases me.' His eyes were tender and very wicked as he ran his warm hand across the smooth mound of her stomach, which was swollen and heavy with child.

'Well, of course, if it pleases you that's all that matters.' She lay back in the bed with the confidence of a woman who knew she was fully and completely loved. 'We must keep you happy at all costs.' The sarcasm delighted him.

'I have never seen you look so beautiful.' His face was serious now and his touch gentle as he joined her under the linen covers, drawing her close into his side.

'That's only because of you, my darling.' As she looked up at him she wondered, for the hundredth, thousandth time since becoming his wife, how she could ever have hesitated for a moment. He had been offering her paradise and she had nearly thrown it all away.

'You are happy, my love?' There was that note of faint anxiety that reared its head now and again and she loved him all the more for it. In answer she pulled his head down to hers, moving her lips across the seared cheek before she found his mouth in a long, deep kiss.

'You are happy.' His arrogance would have made her angry once but now she only felt a deep thankfulness that she had managed to convince him that the past was dead and buried.

'Are you hoping for a boy, Jay?' As her dark grey eyes met the brilliant green of his she saw a small smile flicker for a moment on the firm, warm lips.

'Most certainly.' He pulled her fiercely to him. 'But only because a daughter with your genes in her will be able to twist me round her little finger just as successfully as her mother. My lot in life is difficult enough as it is.' He stroked the silky pale hair back from her forehead before he moved to face her, his dark face deadly serious. 'I only want you, Beth. That is all I have ever wanted. Children are a bonus but only because they are an expression of our love. A little girl would be wonderful—we already have a boy as it is.'

'Mateo?' She smiled lovingly.

'Mateo.' His voice was wry. 'Never have I known a child so attached to another human being as he is to you. I come a very poor second.'

'Do you mind?' She looked at him anxiously.

'Mind?' He laughed out loud now, a deep, joyous sound, and stroked her cheek with a tender finger. 'I can only applaud his excellent taste. Alfredo's son will grow up knowing he is loved and wanted. What more can a child ask?'

She snuggled in satisfied pleasure into his side. She hadn't known, would never have been able to guess, how the mate of *el tigre* was blessed. True love such as they shared was devoid of a struggle for dominance or power, but a sweet, thrilling sharing as two lives became one.

'I can never have enough of you.' His lazy, sensual touch across her swollen breasts caused her to arch against him as his lips teased her ear. 'You think I am very bad?'

'Very bad,' she answered faintly as she locked her fingers behind his head, straining to taste his mouth, asking for the pleasure that only he could give. The fire in his eyes blazed into an inferno as he explored her body with his lips, his dark, coppery skin a moving shadow against her pale smoothness. She was a wife, soon to be a mother, and her cup was full, and *el tigre*, the fierce stranger who was now as necessary to her as eating and breathing, had found his true mate at last.

4 FREE
Romances and 2 FREE gifts just for you!

*You can enjoy all the
heartwarming emotion of true love for FREE!
Discover the heartbreak and happiness,
the emotion and the tenderness of the modern
relationships in Mills & Boon Romances.*

*We'll send you 4 Romances as a special offer
from Mills & Boon Reader Service,
along with the opportunity to have 6 captivating
new Romances delivered to your door each month.*

Claim your FREE books and gifts overleaf...

An irresistible offer from Mills & Boon

Become a regular reader of Romances with Mills & Boon Reader Service and we'll welcome you with 4 books, a CUDDLY TEDDY and a special MYSTERY GIFT all absolutely FREE.

And then look forward to receiving 6 brand new Romances each month, delivered to your door hot off the presses, postage and packing FREE! Plus our free Newsletter featuring author news, competitions, special offers and much more.

This invitation comes with no strings attached. You may cancel or suspend your subscription at any time, and still keep your free books and gifts.

It's so easy. Send no money now. Simply fill in the coupon below and post it to -
Reader Service, FREEPOST, PO Box 236, Croydon, Surrey CR9 9EL.

NO STAMP REQUIRED

Free Books Coupon

Yes! Please rush me 4 FREE Romances and 2 FREE gifts! Please also reserve me a Reader Service subscription. If I decide to subscribe I can look forward to receiving 6 brand new Romances for just £10.80 each month, postage and packing FREE. If I decide not to subscribe I shall write to you within 10 days - I can keep the free books and gifts whatever I choose. I may cancel or suspend my subscription at any time. I am over 18 years of age.

Ms/Mrs/Miss/Mr _____ EP56D

Address _____

_____

Postcode _____ Signature _____

mps MAILING PREFERENCE SERVICE

Forthcoming Titles

DUET
Available in June

The Carole Mortimer Duet   **VELVET PROMISE**
TANGLED HEARTS

The Sally Wentworth Duet   **MISTAKEN WEDDING**
SATAN'S ISLAND

BEST SELLER ROMANCE
Available in July

THE COURSE OF TRUE LOVE Betty Neels
STORM CLOUD MARRIAGE Roberta Leigh

MEDICAL ROMANCE
Available in July

JUST WHAT THE DOCTOR ORDERED Caroline Anderson
LABOUR OF LOVE Janet Ferguson
THE FAITHFUL TYPE Elizabeth Harrison
A CERTAIN HUNGER Stella Whitelaw

Available from W.H. Smith, John Menzies, Martins, Forbuoys, most supermarkets and other paperback stockists.

Also available from Mills & Boon Reader Service, Freepost, P.O. Box 236, Thornton Road, Croydon, Surrey CR9 9EL.

Readers in South Africa - write to:
Book Services International Ltd, P.O. Box 41654, Craighall, Transvaal 2024.

Next Month's Romances

Each month you can choose from a wide variety of romance with Mills & Boon. Below are the new titles to look out for next month, why not ask either Mills & Boon Reader Service or your Newsagent to reserve you a copy of the titles you want to buy — just tick the titles you would like and either post to Reader Service or take it to any Newsagent and ask them to order your books.

Please save me the following titles:	Please tick	✓
THE SEDUCTION OF KEIRA	Emma Darcy	
THREAT FROM THE PAST	Diana Hamilton	
DREAMING	Charlotte Lamb	
MIRRORS OF THE SEA	Sally Wentworth	
LAWFUL POSSESSION	Catherine George	
DESIGNED TO ANNOY	Elizabeth Oldfield	
A WOMAN ACCUSED	Sandra Marton	
A LOVE LIKE THAT	Natalie Fox	
LOVE'S DARK SHADOW	Grace Green	
THE WILLING CAPTIVE	Lee Stafford	
MAN OF THE MOUNTAINS	Kay Gregory	
LOVERS' MOON	Valerie Parv	
CRUEL ANGEL	Sharon Kendrick	
LITTLE WHITE LIES	Marjorie Lewty	
PROMISE ME LOVE	Jennifer Taylor	
LOVE'S FANTASY	Barbara McMahon	

If you would like to order these books in addition to your regular subscription from Mills & Boon Reader Service please send £1.80 per title to: Mills & Boon Reader Service, Freepost, P.O. Box 236, Croydon, Surrey, CR9 9EL, quote your Subscriber No:.................................... (If applicable) and complete the name and address details below. Alternatively, these books are available from many local Newsagents including W.H.Smith, J.Menzies, Martins and other paperback stockists from 9th July 1993.

Name:..

Address:...

....Post Code:........................

To Retailer: If you would like to stock M&B books please contact your regular book/magazine wholesaler for details.

You may be mailed with offers from other reputable companies as a result of this application.
If you would rather not take advantage of these opportunities please tick box ☐